EVOLUTION

IS VOLUME

30

OF THE

Twentieth Century Encyclopedia of Catholicism

UNDER SECTION

III

THE NATURE OF MAN

IT IS ALSO THE

29TH

VOLUME IN ORDER OF PUBLICATION

Edited by *HENRI DANIEL-ROPS* of the Académie Française

EVOLUTION

By RÉMY COLLIN

Translated from the French by J. TESTER

HAWTHORN BOOKS · PUBLISHERS · New York

First Edition, November, 1959

NIHIL OBSTAT

Johannes M. T. Barton, S.T.D., L.S.S.

Censor Deputatus

IMPRIMATUR

E. Morrogh Bernard

Vicarius Generalis

Westmonasterii, die XI SEPTEMBRIS MCMLIX

CONTENTS

NOTE

When Professor Rémy Collin died at the beginning of November 1957, he had not finished this book; in particular there remained a few pages, more scientific than philosophical, to write, for which I have followed as far as I could his notes and the outline he himself had drawn up. I did not think it right that the continuity of the text should be broken by marking in special type those passages which I have had to add to finish his work. The reader will therefore, I trust, impute to me such imperfections of thought or language as he may find in the ensuing pages.

Dr. J. BARRY

INTRODUCTION

THE EVOLUTIONARY TRILOGY

The view of the universe, to which man belongs, held by most contemporary scientists can be likened to a trilogy, the three parts having an increasing human interest: cosmogony (the birth of the universe), biogenesis (the birth of life) and anthropogenesis with noögenesis (the birth of man and of mind). The intellectual thread that runs through this modern trilogy is ancient enough: it is the "Becoming" of Heraclitus, considered as a general principle of explanation, which today inspires the theory of evolution in its various forms. From a very general point of view the theory of evolution is an intellectual construction which attempts to retrace and interpret the changes undergone in the course of time by the corporeal, sensible world; that is, by the physical world as it is presented to our senses, either unaided, or assisted by instruments. To follow a current definition, which will serve for the time being, bodies are material objects having position in space. This definition is applicable to the physical universe of which the earth is part (cosmogony), and to the living things which inhabit the earth, including man (biogenesis and anthropogenesis). The theory of evolution in the usual, narrower sense (in which it is generally used in this book) is that part of the general theory which deals with living things. According to this theory they are made of the same physical stuff as non-living things, and have all descended one from another.

Generally educated and intelligent people know, with varying degrees of exactness, that both in the general and the more restricted sense the theory of evolution is the sort of debatable question from which, as we shall see, it is very difficult to eliminate all subjective elements. Since no one is quite exempt from such subjectivity I shall try to take account of others' views without considering them as naturally opposed to my own. After all, it is very difficult for anyone to see clearly with regard to problems where only some of the facts are known and where even the most honest of men are led to make guesses from whatever information they have. But if it is clearly recognized that the advances of science, in the realm of theory, are often made by trial and error; if it is realized that the scientist desirous of unity and coherence in his ideas nevertheless only has partial truths from which to construct his theory: then it is easily understandable that a scientist must often be affected by some personal factor in formulating his theories.

If I needed briefly to justify these remarks I should choose as my text the last book of an eminent zoologist whom I knew well, Lucien Cuénot, a book[1] which he said summed up his life's work. It is a very fully documented work and is divided into two parts: the known facts, and the uncertainties. That is to say that in 1951, after sixty years' study as an evolutionary biologist (for such he always was), Cuénot still felt the great weight of the uncertainties. In dealing with them he disturbs the philosophical roots of the problem of evolution; he refers to the neo-Darwinism of Julian Huxley and J. B. S. Haldane of Great Britain and of H. J. Muller of the United States. This neo-Darwinism, he wrote, rested on one central idea: the rejection of everything irrational—"things unknown there may be, but not things unknowable"—of any hypothesis of an aim, of an intelligent direction of evolution; in a word, the denial of any teleology. We shall see later that since its beginnings evolutionary theory has never been free from all attachment to philosophy, whether that philosophy be broadly religious, or positivist, or materialist. It must always be affected by philosophical ideas because it treats of the origin and destiny of man. To include man in the theory is to make impossible a strictly and exclusively objective view and to introduce subjective and metaphysical elements.

From time to time someone tries to straighten out this confusion of evolutionary theory with various kinds of metaphysics, and a small scandal disturbs intellectual circles for a

---

[1] *L'Évolution biologique*, Paris, Masson et Cie, 1951.

time without making necessary a profound and real revision of the position. In fact there is here a sort of logical paradox: many scientists recognize the weak points of the evolutionary hypothesis, but the majority remain its supporters for various psychological reasons which they force into the pattern of their scientific thought. So for nearly fifty years men have often spoken of "the crisis of evolutionary theory" without getting past that crisis. Making the problem clear with a determined effort at intellectual calmness may assist towards a solution.

VARIOUS MEANINGS OF THE TERM "EVOLUTION"

In practice the word "evolution" is used in very different senses, generally with some confusion of the ideas contained in these senses. Our first task is therefore one of analysis.

General meaning of the word

In a very general sense which raises no difficulties, "evolution" refers to every change which an observer, even untrained, can record in any category of phenomena—physical, biological or human. The changing nature of the world, its transformation or that of its parts, are commonly accepted facts.

The attribution of a meaning to this change

Prolonged observation of phenomena which seem to be linked together generally leads the scientist to give them a meaning, and at this point is introduced a concept of value. We shall give two examples of this, one from biology and the other from physics.

(a) *Progressive evolution:* Palaeontology tells us that in different geological periods there successively appeared living forms of ever greater complexity, up to man with his intellectual, moral and social faculties. The observed changes are progressive, if referred to a more or less high standard of perfection, and the evolution is described as *orthogenetic*,[2] which is to say, a development which occurs in a predetermined, chosen direction.

[2] The idea of orthogenesis is fully discussed later.

(b) *Regressive evolution:* The second law of thermodynamics
is thus expressible: if a change can spontaneously occur by a
transformation involving the action of heat then the reverse of
that change cannot occur spontaneously. This way of expressing
it makes clear the fact that the changes undergone by the parts
of an isolated physical system are irreversible and end in a
state of equilibrium, the energy level of which is lower than
that of the initial state. In this sense one speaks of the running-
down of energy, which corresponds to a measurable quantity
called *entropy.* Jean Perrin called the second law of thermodynamics the principle of evolution, and in this case the
evolution is regressive.

Theorizing about the facts of evolution

The facts of evolution once established, an explanation is
sought which will satisfy them by fitting them into a system
we call a theory. It might be worth while to recall briefly how
in general scientific theories are formed.

(a) *Two sources of scientific theories:* Scientific theories have
two connected and indispensable sources: a collection of facts
which appear to be ordered, and an original spark in the mind
of the scientist that one calls an intuition, an imaginative fore-
sight that finds expression first as an hypothesis, that is, a
supposition as to what is true. Notice that at this stage in the
formulation of a theory there is, whether we like it or not, an
element of subjectivity which cannot be neglected. It cannot be
neglected because it is the leaven of inventiveness. The leaven
is what makes something rise—dough, for example. In intellectual matters, and especially in the sciences, the dough is the
collection of brute facts which, to be assimilated and to become
intelligible, need to be submitted to a process of fermentation
in which the mind is itself the principal active ingredient.

On the basis of the first hypothesis, still uncertain but allow-
ing of experimental verification, little by little a theory can be
constructed. A scientific theory is an intellectual representation
of a collection of facts, a synthesis; and this representation has
the greater truth, the greater effectiveness, as it gathers together

a greater number of already-established facts and allows the prediction of the conditions for the realizing of others not yet established. It has been said, though it applies particularly to the physical sciences—astronomy, physics and chemistry—that contemporary science spreads a net of mathematical relations intended to embrace all the data furnished by experimental techniques, and it is the whole of the net that science intends to compare with the sum of the data. Some famous examples of physical theories of this kind are the classical mechanics of Newton, the quantum theory of Planck, the theory of general relativity of Einstein and the wave mechanics of Louis de Broglie.

Still it must not be forgotten that every theory, however satisfactory it may be, or appear to be, always remains subject to the tests of observation and experiment. A theory is a verified hypothesis, after it has undergone the checks of reasoning and experimental criticism. But for a theory to stay a good one it must always be modified as science progresses, and always remain subject to verification and the criticism of new facts which may appear. This reservation must always be made. Scientific theories can be either more or less well established. Instruments of the truth, they bring truth to light. Yet they never bring us complete intellectual certainty. Better than any-one else, the scientist knows that in his own field, limited to a part of the sensible world which may be more or less important, even as knowledge advances it continually discloses to him areas of the unknown, and so forces him again and again without any foreseeable end to refashion his work. This work derives its worth from a permanent hope, never altogether deceived, never completely satisfied, despite whatever success it may achieve. A corollary follows from what we have said. Even the most advanced scientific theories never represent more than a passing momentary stage in the history of man's thought, and are moreover always likely to be left behind. Nor must they ever be confused with absolute truths or transformed into unshakable dogmas. They merely mark an ideal course, plotting the direction by a kind of foreknowledge of an absolute truth the fragments of which are precious enough to awaken a sense of vocation in the scientist and to sustain him on a road beset with difficulties.

We talk of *good* theories because although they may not give us all the truth, at least they convey to us some truths which are as stimulating to the mind as they are able to increase man's control of nature. And one may wonder whether their merits and their success are not closely linked to that feeling of humility that made Louis de Broglie say: "There is far more of a mystery than is usually believed in the simple fact that a little science is possible at all."[3]

(b) *Subjective overvaluation of some scientific theories:* One of the commonest traps that scientists fall into is the temptation to extrapolate and attribute to their theories an absolute, universal value, transforming them in this way into myths. We shall examine later the relations between scientific theories and metaphysics, but here and now we should like to call the reader's attention to a certain misuse of the idea of a theory. We refer to a kind of conceptual overvaluation which makes a particular science claim more than is warranted by the facts actually coordinated by it. This distortion is especially evident in the case of the doctrine of biological evolution, which postulates that all living things come one from another, without a break in the line of inheritance. We must not forget at this point that the assertions of a good working theory are always conditional, and often take the form: things happen *as if* . . . which has the advantage of not hardening the scientist into an immobility of mind incompatible with new discovery. Now in the case of evolution there has been for all its hundred years a gap, of varying importance, between the known facts and their theoretical interpretation—this last often representing if not an extrapolation at least a risky anticipation. Some famous scientists, carried away by a conviction strongly coloured by subjectiveness, have not hesitated to claim that evolution is not an hypothesis of greater or less probability, but a solidly established fact. Let us agree that when he is dealing with palaeon-

[3] *L'Invention, IXe Sem. intern. de synthèse,* Paris, Alcan, 1937.

tology the biologist is less strictly forbidden any subjective interpretation than the physicist is, who must submit his actual experimental results to the formal test of mathematics. It is true that the biologist has no less than the physicist real facts to deal with, but for the study of physical facts of such antiquity he has only the very imperfect method of going back over the ground, over the list of the relics of living forms which inhabited the earth during the millions of years of the past, a list which all agree is very far from complete. In these circumstances any claim that evolution is a *fact* constitutes an extrapolation, even today, and must be at least provisionally rejected until the proofs have been shown.

As much must be said of the position of Teilhard de Chardin in his posthumous book, *Le Phénomène humain*.[4] He expresses the view that evolution is "the universal law of the cosmos" and says: "Is evolution a theory, or a system, or an hypothesis? Not at all: it is much more than that, it is a general condition which from now on, if they are to be conceivable or true, all theories, all hypotheses and all systems must conform to and satisfy. It is a light illuminating all facts, a curve which must pass through all points; that is what evolution is." A little later he adds: "What makes a man modern (and in this sense a lot of our contemporaries are not yet modern!) is having become capable of seeing not only in space, not only in time, but in duration—or what comes to the same thing, biological space-time—and in addition being incapable of seeing anything, *anything*, otherwise, beginning with himself." Let us register in passing a reservation concerning the assimilation of a "modern" man to an unconditional supporter of the whole theory of evolution.

Moreover I think that when a modern scientist reflects on his intellectual position he humbles himself and often recognizes that he will leave this world before resolving all the enigmas: for science is inexhaustible. But we also know that

[4] Editions du Seuil, Paris, 1955. While this book was in the press an English translation of Fr Teilhard de Chardin's work was announced. See Select Bibliography at the end of this volume.

"a little science is possible". This is why, considering that the cosmos as a whole and our earth in particular do present the phenomena of evolution, we cannot reject the legitimate claims of a theory of evolution as a means of investigating nature. But we must remember that every scientific theory is incomplete by definition and can only ever offer us an imperfect likeness of the universe. Let us also remember that the physical scientist always has before his mind the fact that a theory is only true to a certain degree of approximation; it is always susceptible of revision as the analysis of the universe becomes more and more complete. In any case, the theory of evolution begins from the supposition that a necessary link exists between the various phenomena of the universe.

Creation and evolution

It often happens that the ideas of creation and evolution are opposed to one another. The first seems bound to ideas characterized pejoratively as dogmatic; the second is inseparable from the notion of change. In fact, the usual idea of creation belongs to the domain of religion, since it has its source in Judaeo-Christian revelation. Properly speaking it has nothing to do with any scientific theory, since a scientific theory is first and foremost a research tool in the realm of the sensible world, not a dogma. But it must be said that at a certain stage of their researches scientists find themselves asking questions concerning the origins and the ends of things, and it is legitimate for them to seek to answer those questions. But then they must recognize that they are going beyond the normal field of their researches. The religious idea of creation can be rationally justified by metaphysical reasoning. Such reasoning shows that a sound definition of creation is independent of theories of biology, whether evolutionary or holding to the simultaneous origin of all species, in that it can fit in with either. In fact the idea of creation, dissociated from adventitious notions which sometimes alter it (for example, questions concerning the finitude or infinity of the cosmos from a temporal point of view, as well as from that of space), is reduced to a unilateral relation of dependence of the created world, which is temporal, on its Creator, who is eternal.

God has no history. He is. But what is created evolves, because it is imperfect and is in process of realizing its own potentiality. Its createdness is a participation, and to say "participation" is to say also "imperfection", with the tendency towards, and consequent search for, the perfect. Now the relation between the past and the present, and between the present and the future, is just that between possibility and existence, and between actual existence and another kind of existence. This is the characteristic of the imperfect, which comes from the Perfect, and which is independent because distinguished by its imperfection from its Source, on condition that it perfects itself by its development in its own existence in time, which is the necessary condition of its possible self-perfection.

CHAPTER I

COSMOGONY

When a modern scientist considers the *beginnings* of physical phenomena he admits, whatever his philosophical opinions, the succession: cosmogony, biogenesis, anthropogenesis. We shall return to the idea of beginning, which raises a problem which some pantheists resolve by the ancient conception of an eternal cyclic process. To stay on firm ground, the cosmos, as it appears today, seems to scientists to be the result of three major changes which succeed each other in time: the evolution of the pre-stellar and stellar universe, or physical cosmogony; the evolution of the world of living things, or biogenesis; and the evolution of man, or anthropogenesis. These distinctions are valid for all contemporary minds and are sufficiently general not to raise any difficulty of a scientific or philosophical order. Nevertheless, before we go any further it must be said that in fact these three worlds of inanimate nature, of living things, and of man, coexist on earth with certain necessary connections. Again, the earth itself, considered as a whole or in its parts, is united with the rest of the cosmos by links of energy or matter which are not unimportant. This is what gives us the idea that the earth and its inhabitants are formed from the same material stuff as the rest of the universe, an idea now demonstrated in the results of astrophysics.

COSMOGONY IN GENERAL

When a scientist speaks of cosmogony he is expressing implicitly or explicitly a historical concept. He is postulating an arbitrary point t_0 starting from which he seeks to describe the cosmic events that have led from t_0 to the present. In reality he does not know exactly the distance in time of t_0; he tries to interpret the coming-to-be of the physical world as it was by means of points of reference furnished by his knowledge of the world as it is, a knowledge which is always incomplete but which gives him some parameters to use in interpreting the past. Spectrography, for example, allows him to infer that the matter or stuff of the universe is the same in all its parts; in other words, that all the celestial bodies, whatever their physical state at any given time, are made of the same chemical elements as the earth in which the observers are placed.

With these conditions, we can imagine at the beginning of our universe an enormous cloud of sub-atomic particles, or of atoms of masses corresponding to those of Mendeleyev's periodic classification.* At the present day, after the spectrographic researches of the American astronomer Hubble at Mount Wilson, it is known that the nebulae are receding from our galaxy* at a speed proportional to their distance from us. This is mathematically deduced from the shift of the spectrum towards the red end noticeable when spectra from more and more distant objects are compared. We know also that the measurements of Hubble led Canon Lemaître of Louvain to formulate in 1927 the theory of the expanding universe, which supposes that there was at the beginning of time a monstrous primitive atom, of enormous density, which exploded and gave birth to all the matter now scattered over the universe. The theory of expansion moreover represents, in the framework of the general theory of relativity, one of the possibilities of evolution of the hyperspheric, unstable universe of Einstein, the end of such an evolution being the empty hyperbolic universe of de Sitter. Nevertheless, various insufficiencies in our documentation and certain difficulties of theorization make it premature to hold as definitely demonstrated this or that par-

* Words so marked will be found in the Glossary at the end of this volume.

ticular cosmogony, since a whole series of tenable intermediate positions is strung out between the extremes of a steady-state theory of the universe limited *a parte ante* and *a parte post*, and of a pulsating universe the cyclic evolution of which would present the advantage (claimed, but only apparent!) of freeing the human mind of the difficult problems of the origin and end of the universe.

To restrict ourselves to questions more within our grasp, astronomy, basing itself on the analysis of radio-active minerals in the crust of the earth, evaluates what may be described as the age of our planet. The atoms of most of the heavier elements are unstable and spontaneously disintegrate into lighter ones with the emission of alpha-particles (helium nuclei), beta-particles (electrons) and gamma-rays.* The lighter elements so formed are also generally unstable and disintegrate in their turn after a varying period of time, and so on to the last element formed, which is stable. This element is in all cases lead, to which the three radio-active families of uranium, thorium and actinium all degenerate. For example, in one year one and a half ten-millionths ($1 \cdot 5 \times 10^{-7}$) of any given mass of uranium will have changed to lead. From all this the ages of ancient rocks are calculated to be of the order of $1 \cdot 5$ to 2×10^9 (one and a half to two thousand million) years. This is the minimum age for the solidified earth's crust; to obtain the age of the earth an undetermined period of cooling must be added, estimated at several hundred million years. This gives as the age of the earth a possible value of about three thousand million years (3×10^9). The most exact value given, after all refinements, is $3 \cdot 25 \times 10^9$ years. Today it is generally agreed that one can attribute to the whole universe an age equal to or scarcely greater than that of the earth, though this would have seemed most unlikely even so little as twenty years ago.

According to the astronomers we can with the means of investigation we possess today only take a "sample", of the order of size of a twentieth, of the radius of the whole universe. Now the size of the universe is measured in light-years and one light-year is the distance light travels, at approximately 186,000

miles a second, in one year, or nearly six million million miles.
For example the great nebula in Andromeda, which is one of
our neighbouring galaxies, is about a million and a half light-
years away. These few figures give us some idea of the bewilder-
ing size of the universe and, by comparison, of the relative
littleness of the astronomical system of which we are a part.
Relative to some dimensions of the universe which have been
worked out the sun is a small star, the earth an infinitesimally
small speck of a planet, and a man a microbe (in the etymological sense). Yet man is capable of comprehending the universe and of unravelling little by little its laws.

What cannot be doubted is that the universe of astronomy,
as we know it today, is continually changing. Astrophysicists
talk of the births and histories and deaths of stars, and classify
them according to their size as dwarfs, giants and supergiants,
or according to their temperatures into blue (with luminosities
a hundred thousand times the sun's), red (luminosities not
exceeding one thousand times the sun's) and yellow (like our
sun). The supergiants draw their energy from the transmutation
of their hydrogen, which constitutes eighty per cent of their
mass. They use their stock of combustible material at a prodigious rate, and despite their enormous masses cannot keep up
this mode of life for more than a hundred million years or so.
Those we now see must therefore be quite young and have
been formed in the tertiary era or even nearer to our own age:
they are our contemporaries. There is no reason to believe that
they are not even today still being formed. What brings them
into being, of what materials? Perhaps the interstellar dust.
Some astrophysicists draw attention to the small black globular
nebulosities in some quarters of the sky, which may be stars
in process of formation. There are also stars of enormous
volume but very low temperature which could be the end
products of such globular nebulae and the beginnings of what
are properly called stars.

There is no room in this book to give more facts of this kind,
but those already given, although incomplete, nevertheless
support the notion that the sidereal universe changes with time,

or evolves. But when we consider the course of the earth's history separately we do not know in what direction it is evolving or how the two laws of thermodynamics come into play. Nor do we know whether life has appeared on some other planet than our own, in one of the millions of galaxies that have been observed. In fact, what we call astrophysics is a science trying to explain sidereal phenomena and those of interstellar matter by the physical principles and laws of our world, which essentially apply to inanimate bodies, and we have no real reason to suppose that there are two different physical categories in the universe of which the earth is a part. On the contrary, everything leads us to assume that the whole universe, considered as a coherent system, is the same in its composition of energy and matter. So we feel quite comfortable about dealing with the history of the earth as giving us a precise physical model which man may dare to apply to the whole cosmos.

THE BEGINNING OF THE LITHOSPHERE AND THE HYDROSPHERE

Whatever be the supposed original state, whether a limitless cloud of sub-atomic particles or atoms or an enormous hyperdense atom which explodes in a cloud to produce the kind of universe it must, the physico-chemical analysis of the matter that constitutes our planet and its inhabitants forces us to imagine a moment when the particles gathered together to form dense bodies. The physicists, and after them the geologists, have managed to present to us a fairly satisfying picture of the origins of the earth's crust, which is called the lithosphere. It is thought that the primitive mass of material elements which must have constituted the earth reached a very high temperature and that the crust was formed by cooling, by the condensation on the surface of a sea of fused minerals, whence were deposited in turn a layer of discontinuous rock called *sial* by Suess (*si*licon-*al*uminium) and a layer of *sima* (*si*licon-*ma*gnesium). The melting point of aluminium is 653° C, that of magnesium 633° C, which gives an idea of the temperature required for the formation of a lithosphere. As the cooling of the earth continued and the surface temperature cooled to below 100° C the water vapour surrounding it condensed and formed the seas in the depressions which separated the first continents.

The descriptions suggested for the development of the lithosphere and the hydrosphere, and of the atmosphere also, and the hypotheses formulated concerning their developmental relationships, are too uncertain to allow us yet to fill in details. It is however generally agreed that the primitive atmosphere was different from the present one, the oxygen in which seems to be the result of the activity of living things. What we know of the phenomena of life and especially of the upper and lower temperature limits within which it is possible at all, shows that the appearance of life was preceded by a long geological history. The beginnings of life must have been before the Cambrian era, a short time ago compared with the time needed to lower the temperature to a level compatible with the existence of living things. Yet certain recent estimations lead us to consider it not unlikely that life appeared at a very remote distance in time, perhaps some two thousand million years ago. This problem is considered in the next chapter.

CHAPTER II

BIOGENESIS, OR THE BIRTH OF LIFE

Science supposes that life developed from inanimate matter by a purely physical process. Let us leave this claim on one side for the time being, while recognizing straight away that living things, or more exactly the bodies of living things, are made of the same elements as inanimate objects. Nevertheless, a new physical entity appeared with life. It is not a matter of breaking the laws of inanimate matter: these remain valid on the biological level. It is a matter of the birth of a new arrangement of the world of matter, in the sense that the analytical study of animate beings uncovers what we may call anthropomorphically a choice, or from another point of view, a complication. But first let us see what palaeontology tells us.

THE GAPS IN THE EARLIEST RECORDS

Between the formation of the lithosphere and hydrosphere and the appearance of living things there is a gap which it seems cannot be filled. The first fossil traces of living things, of the pre-Cambrian era, consist in a collection of various organisms, some of which are already differentiated zoologically. Beside the bacteria, calcareous algae, and foraminifera, there are the coelenterates, molluscs and crustacea of enormous size. In the most ancient known rocks there are already found very varied forms, including trilobites, and a great number and variety of animals, even some in a fairly advanced state of organization. All the older rocks were destroyed by meta-morphosis* and crystallized by this melting and mixing at a high temperature. There are only a few vague signs left to show that there was life before. Palaeontology takes up the story at a point when life was already established in a number of very varied forms. The pre-Cambrian world was therefore already far evolved and probably considerably later than the age of the origins of life. The palaeontologist is unable to tell us in what form living things first appeared, for he only gets hold of a species when its extension is great and its history well advanced—that is, at a time already a long way from its origin. This short summary, which could easily be expanded, gives the opinion of the great majority of scientists in this field and could safely be taken to express a definitive conclusion: that the problem of the origins of life, strictly from the point of view of the natural sciences, must be attacked on different lines. These lead in fact to geo-chemistry (the problem of the actual origin of living from non-living matter) and to "bio-poietics"—experiments in making living things in the labora-tory (the problem of the synthesis of living matter). But before we look at these we must recall briefly the principal biological and chemical characteristics of living things.

CHARACTERISTICS OF LIVING THINGS

Biological properties

In our experience life is always produced from life—as William Harvey expressed it, *omne vivum ex ovo*: the propa-gation of living things being effected by one of two modes of reproduction, asexual or sexual. Clearly we cannot here draw up an exhaustive table of the phenomena of life, either of vegetative or locomotive life. We shall mention only these two cardinal properties, assimilation and reproduction. For the scientist the individual living thing is a corporeal form, dis-tinguished from other corporeal forms called inanimate by the fact that it subordinates and uses these others for a certain period of time before itself returning to an inanimate, mineral state. From birth to death a living creature takes sustenance of mineral, vegetable or animal origin from the external environment, which it transforms and assimilates; that is to say, it changes this food into its own substance and rejects into the external environment the waste products of its unceasing chemical activity.

Again, just as it is capable of assimilation, that is of growing, of maintaining and keeping its own substance together for some period of time, so a living thing is by one mechanism of reproduction or the other the ensurer of life's perpetuity: life is now a permanent feature of the material world. Living things which multiply by asexual reproduction die only by accident; they are thus endowed with potential immortality. Those reproducing sexually die, but continue their existence in their descendants which are born of part of themselves, the fertilized egg. The stream of life in which we are ourselves immersed seems to us everlasting. To end this short account of the biological properties of assimilation and reproduction it might be allowed to us, without our appearing simply to be playing upon words, to express the following conclusions: assimilation reproduces in a given creature something of what was existing before, namely its own substance; on the other hand reproduction, in the usual sense of the word, is a kind of assimilation, for the matter taken up to make the generation which is produced is assimilated to the form of that which produces it.

Chemical properties

Passing on to the physico-chemical field we know that the composition of living things needs only a very small proportion of the known natural chemical elements, and that these few are among those having the smallest atomic numbers. Living matter is thus remarkable at first glance in that it only utilizes a small number of chemical elements. But to make up for this the molecules made out of this small number of elements attain dimensions and weights unknown in the world of inanimate nature. Compare for example a molecule of water (H_2O) with a macromolecule * from a living thing, ovalbumin: the first has a molecular weight of eighteen, the second one of 34,500—over nineteen hundred times that of the water molecule. Biochemists deal with molecular arrangements very much larger than ovalbumin with weights of over a million. In short, from relatively light atoms are constructed the heavy molecules characteristic of living things, which suggests that these molecules have a very complicated structure. The complexity of the individual living creature does not stop at the macromolecular level, however. The macromolecule is only one of the hundreds of materials, all different and some not specific to living matter (water, the salts, oxygen, carbon dioxide), which go together to make up the various structures which are hierarchically ordered and integrated.

All the macromolecules entering into the constitution of living things, from the smallest to the largest, include as a characteristic substance a nucleoprotein,* formed of a nucleic acid * and a large protein itself made up of amino-acids * joined together. The nucleic acid is made up in its turn of a phosphoric acid, a pentose (a sugar with five atoms of carbon), and nitrogenous bases. Biochemists have stressed the importance of these nucleoproteins, for all bodies made from them enjoy the astonishing property of self-reproduction, and play an essential part in the phenomena of heredity. This explains why the consideration of their properties has taken the place of the old ideas of a gliodic * protoplasm in the approach to the problem of the emergence of living matter and the synthesis of living things.

THE PROBLEM OF THE EMERGENCE OF LIVING FROM INANIMATE MATTER

Living things are made of the same stuff as the rest of the universe. In other words, they appeared at a given time in the story of the earth, when the earth's material elements had reached a state comparable to that which we know today. Life's appearance brought into being a new state of matter, superimposed on the lithosphere, hydrosphere and atmosphere. These last subsist, of course, and relations have been established between them and the newly arrived living things. We are now certain that our planet passed through a lifeless state before the appearance of living things, and we are also certain that these are formed of the same chemical elements as inanimate bodies, with this distinction, that only a few of the hundred and one elements known to chemistry enter into their composition. And lastly, we know that the chemical molecules characterizing living things are far more complex than those the chemist finds in inanimate nature.

Life can only exist between narrow limits of temperature variation and it is obvious that in the pre-geological, cosmic stage of our planet's story this small tolerability of temperature changes of such delicate organisms makes their existence impossible. Life appeared at a quite definite epoch in the geochemical development of the earth, and the problem of its origin, a short time ago relegated to the domain of metaphysics, is today set precisely and unavoidably before us as scientific. Modern physics, which has put into the melting-pot the conceptions of thousands of years—such as time and space—today pushes the boundaries of metaphysics further and further back, successfully attacking the problems of the atoms, the stars, the cosmogony of the solar system, the evolution of the universe. The problem of life cannot remain unaffected by this upheaval. It has been claimed in fact that it is a purely physical problem. We may agree with this claim, that it is purely a problem for the physical sciences, if in order to study it appeal is made only to physical data. But this is a matter of convention, a rule of the scientific game, whose value in finding explanations we know from other examples, in the sense that when such a scientific explanation is reached we can reproduce certain natural phenomena. Chemical synthesis, for example, arranges in the way they are wanted chemicals previously isolated by analysis. But we shall maintain later that scientific synthesis, even when it is brilliant and opens wide horizons to our view, never corresponds to the total explanation to which the human mind aspires. Let us merely mark in passing that the monist position postulated by the scientist's method requires, whether it is explicitly avowed or not, a metaphysics—a negative metaphysics if you like, but a metaphysics all the same. We shall return to this, but for now let us see what can be gained from physics.

First, the problem of life is divided into two problems of unequal difficulty. The first, on the level of physics and geochemistry, refers to the evolution of organic matter from inorganic; the second, much more complex, refers to the elaboration of organic structures, and constitutes the transition from geochemistry to cytology.*

Evolution of organic from inorganic matter

It is conceivable that relatively *simple* organic substances were formed by the action of the ultra-violet rays in sunlight from the primitive atmosphere, although agreement on the exact composition of that atmosphere has not yet been reached. The number of theoretical explanations proposed, which we cannot here set out in detail, shows that any or all of several processes may have played a part. That these processes could work is proved by various experiments, notably by those recently performed by Miller in the United States, in which he obtained certain amino-acids from a mixture of carbon dioxide, methane and ammonia by passing an electric discharge through it. On the other hand, it is obviously more difficult to account for the appearance of dissymmetric organic compounds such as characterize living matter, whether their appearance be the result of an instantaneous completely asymmetric synthesis or of the division into two of a pre-existing racemic* compound. Any asymmetric process, whether local (circularly polarized light, the polar force of absorption in certain mineral aggregates, the epitaxis* of some crystals) or cosmic (direction of rotation of the earth, terrestrial magnetism, etc.), *could* in principle interfere to render this or that synthesis more likely, or such and such division. Interference of this kind seems, however, so unlikely that some prefer to appeal to some chance

coincidence giving rise, by a photo-chemical reaction with
either visible or ultra-violet light, to a trace of an active substance which then played the part of a dissymmetric catalyst.

From organic matter to organisms

Although there is some disagreement as to the lowest limit
above which it is right to talk of a living thing (rudimentary
organisms like viruses or infra-cellular organisms like microbes
or bacteria being near the lower limits) most writers agree in
thinking that the organic matter which appeared as the result
of the earth's geochemical evolution gathered in certain regions
of the lithosphere or on the surface or in the depths of the
hydrosphere (in the primitive lakes or oceans according to the
theory), some of these compounds being in a metastable*
structural state. In a further stage of development, and perhaps after a very long period in which various configurations
emerged which were biologically unsuccessful and fruitless, the
first "organized" nucleo-protein macromolecules endowed with
the powers of self-reproduction and assimilation would have
emerged from some of these metastable organic compounds.
The factors determining this development are only to be
guessed at—thermic agitation, valency forces, photochemical
reactions, etc.—and their probable effectiveness incapable of
being precisely stated, in view of our ignorance of the exact
composition and structure of the supposed environment. After
a final period, further subdivided into a series of stages each
of which probably corresponds with the appearance of another
degree of material complexity, organic forms of pre-cellular
type (protocaryota*) or truly cellular (caryota) would have been
progressively separated out, after repeated processes of isolation or delimitation. These forms would no doubt, though here
again we do not know, have been based on the formation of
mono- or poly-molecular layers serving as successive membranes. During this last period, ending with the formation of
true unicellular organisms (Protista), photosynthesising* autotrophic* organisms would have been developed. The primitive
atmosphere would thus have been enriched by the oxygen these

first organisms released and so have provided a protective layer of ozone to cut off from their more highly developed descendants the lethal action of the sun's ultra-violet radiation of wave-lengths greater than 2,900 Angstrom units.*

We cannot within the scope of this summary give the details of the various hypothetical stages from organic matter to organism. But we note first that the appearance of "organized" nucleoprotein macromolecules raises the problem of the conditions which allowed them to persist and develop by simple heterotrophy,* while the now known representatives of this type of organization—that is, the viruses—are so far as is at present known always strictly limited to the conditions of intracellular parasitism. Secondly, once the first living things have appeared, their characteristic property of utilizing the matter and the energy of the external environment should, within certain limits of composition of that environment, assure the permanence of life on earth. "Just as the discontinuities of quanta play an essential part in the building and stability of atomic and molecular structures, it is certain now that they also ensure the stability of the macromolecules which form the elements of living structures, and that they underlie the wonderful permanence of life throughout and surpassing the lives of individuals and of successive generations."[1] Thirdly and lastly, if the preceding stages of the genesis of living organisms really "subdivide" the difficulties raised by the problem of their natural origin from inorganic matter, they must not blind us to the perfectly real "enormity" of this problem, an enormity the more impressed on modern scientists because the very recent researches of the last few years into the "fine structure" of living things with the aid of the electron microscope have shown us the extreme delicacy and complexity of their architecture,[2] with dimensions of the order of between a few Angstrom units and a few hundred (even if their basis is

[1] L. de Broglie, in "Qu'est-ce que la vie?", *Nouvelles Littéraires*, March 2nd, 1950.
[2] A remarkable account has been given by Engstrom and Finean under the title, *Biological Ultrastructure*; 326 pp., Academic Press, New York, February, 1958.

frequently repeated, as it is for example for the various generally bilamellar cytomembranes*). To such a point is this true that it seems we may say that the complexity of intra-cellular organisms long described by the classical techniques of cytology now extends into the infra-micronic* level. The result of this is that the attitude of those pursuing these re-searches, even the most positivist, oscillates between two extreme and firm assertions, of the high objective improbability of there being living things at all, and a methodological necessity for an origin of life since living things do certainly exist and therefore there *must* have been an origin. It is miraculous that conditions should have so arranged themselves as to make life possible, and not at all surprising if such a miracle only happened once; but however miraculous it may appear, the beginning of life was *an event of the natural order*.

THE CHANCE ORIGIN OF LIFE

If a human observer had by a miracle lived in the lifeless period of the earth's history, he would not have been able to predict the birth of life on the basis of his knowledge of the mineral world, supposing his knowledge to have been as advanced as that of a contemporary chemist. Now at a given moment life came into being, at the expense of some inanimate matter. If we say that life exists because of the chance meeting of certain material substances, we are forced to admit that without that chance meeting life would not have appeared. The objection to this suggestion is that our minds seem incapable of admitting that so tremendous a phenomenon as the birth of life should have been due to the fortuitous conjunction of a few material particles. For life is before our eyes, not doubt-fully existing, but a plainly organized system obeying laws as pressing as those of the world of physics. Is it scientifically possible that the determinism of the inorganic world and the determinism of the world of life are linked only by the slender thread of chance? In a word, for fear of mixing metaphysical notions with scientific facts, we introduce even into science itself a *deus ex machina*, the chance origin of life.

There is fortunately another solution of this problem. It was found in modern times by a famous positivist, Emile Littré, precisely in connection with the origins of life. The "Open, Sesame!" of Littré was a sound idea, not unknown to the Scholastics, and is valid as much for science as for philosophy: it is the idea of *predetermination*. In the same way, he said, as the chemical properties of matter, when the circumstances are such as are needed for their manifestation, appear with their inherent predeterminations—that is, simple or combined crystal-line forms—so the vital property of matter, when the circum-stances are such as are needed for its manifestation, obeys the predeterminations inherent in itself, that is, functional organiza-tion. When he expressed these ideas Littré considered that the connection of life with organization and of organization with life was what made, for the time being, the question of the origin of living things on the earth's surface insoluble. We appear to have got a little further now, in that our con-temporaries have made progress in the chemical explanation of the phenomena of life. But the chemical explanation is still dominated by the more general idea of predetermination, which is valid for the succession of interconnected physical phenomena. It thus becomes important to make more precise just what is understood by predetermination.

Now in its uses "predetermination" has two meanings, a physical and a metaphysical, which there is no need to confuse. In the first sense it is quite simply a potential determination. Or if we wish to avoid the ambiguous anthropomorphism of the word "determination", it is a determinism in potentiality only: that is, something that does not yet exist but that can come into existence. The idea of potentiality is familiar to physicists, who speak of potential energy, for example; they say without wondering about it that the energy of a particle m_0 of matter measures the change we should get as the return for the total annihilation of m_0 grams of matter, namely an energy of twenty-five million kilowatt-hours per gram. Physical predetermination is found everywhere in nature: it is already bound up in the properties of the smallest material entities. Sub-atomic particles have determinate characteristic properties. Now these determinate properties are at the same time predetermined to something else, since under the influence of certain extraneous factors they can give place to a new determination of their characteristics. For example, without going beyond the limits of what is scientifically allowable, we might say that the activity of uranium atoms is predetermined by the sub-atomic particles which enter into their composition. Now in handling the concept of predetermination, in the purely physical sense, one is automatically led to think of chance as the hidden mainspring of the cosmos. The ideas of chance and cosmos (that is, a harmonious ordering of the universe) together imply a contradiction which we shall examine later.

In the particular case of the natural origin of life the chief problem is that of the transition from the reaction to external forces which characterizes inanimate objects to the immanent action which characterizes living things. Now the hypothesis of a chance origin implies that the appearance of life on earth, or in other words of a new category of phenomena, is not the result of any *intention*, of the intervention of any Mind foreign to the world as we can imagine it before life appeared, but is the result of the chance meeting of certain physico-chemical constituents of the world. There is nothing improper about this supposition from the viewpoint of the positivist scientist, for he, by a convention going back to Auguste Comte, rejects all consideration of the question of an absolute Beginning or a first Cause. There are, however, various considerations which lead us to think that the particular characteristics of the immanent action of living things only find their true explanation in the recognition of the mark of intelligence in natural things and especially in living things. To assert this, purely and simply, is to assert a *de facto* finality. The consequence of analysing the implications of this *de facto* finality is the attribution to it of a supernatural origin and its definition simply as the intention of God written into things.

ORGANIC SYNTHESIS[3]

The idea of the artificial production of living things is very old and goes back at least to the alchemists; but it was only slowly separated from its magical context. The positive achievement of the numberless attempts towards this end, some childish or over-simple, others over-elaborate, is practically nil if the results of the last few years are left out of consideration. In fact, it was not until the chemists knew the architecture of nucleo-protein molecules sufficiently well that it occurred to them to synthesize in the hope that success in synthesis would lead one day to a still more astounding synthesis, of a complete and self-sufficient living being. Since 1955 this hope rests on the work of two scientists of the University of California, Fraenkel-Conrat and Williams, on an active virus of the tobacco mosaic. These two scientists succeeded in reconstituting the virus from its proper parts which had previously been separated, namely the specific desoxyribonucleic acid (DNA)* and its protein jacket. Though this is admittedly only partial, since it depends on using natural nucleic and protein parts, already highly complex, nevertheless it is extremely interesting and important. It is true to say that it is no longer beyond the scope of scientists in a laboratory to make artificially beings endowed with the essential properties of life; or, in particular, to make infra-cellular organisms analogous to genes or viruses capable of self-reproduction. So it is not unreasonable to conceive of some artificial generation of life.

Moreover, from very recent (1957) observations it appears that nucleic acid from certain viruses, separated from all protein and thus "pure" as far as we can judge with our present

[3] The study of bacteriophages* by various techniques has made possible the collection of a great deal of illuminating knowledge of the process of self-reproduction, the exchanges of genetic units, etc.; so too has the study of dwarf forms of the L-cycle (elementary body) of certain bacteria, which become uncultivable in protein-rich environments and cultivable only intra-cellularly. We should go beyond the limits of this summary if we took account of all these facts but we have at least used the conclusions that can be drawn from them.

criteria, is capable of self-reproducing *in a living environment*. From the biochemist's standpoint, the first effective stage on the road to synthesizing living matter would therefore be the artificial production of macromolecules of nucleic acid. The very real difficulties, scientific as well as technical, of this should not be underestimated; but neither should they be beyond the possibilities we can reasonably expect of biochemistry in its future development. In a second stage, undoubtedly more problematic, it would be necessary, artificially or semi-artificially, to realize environmental conditions (particular organic substances acting as special receptors, or materials for synthesis; various enzymes being present, etc.) such that the synthetic nucleic acid molecules could employ their powers of using the matter about them. These powers are as yet hypothetical, since natural nucleic acids only possess them in an environment *already* living. Even supposing that the biophysicists and biochemists triumphantly continue to make such progress as they have been making in recent years, it still remains doubtful, for whatever reasons, whether man will ever be able to create synthetic beings even remotely approaching those which we put in the higher categories of our classification. It is even fair to say that if account is to be taken of the extraordinary complexity of cellular organization it would be almost as marvellous to create one cell as to create a plant or an animal that could be seen with the naked eye.

In any case the problem of the artificial generation of life, if one suppose it solved, has the merit of making clear the logical, and indeed experimental, necessity of this fact, that physico-chemical life-producing factors are informed by an external psychic life-producing factor. It is in that case reasonable to wonder whether the eventual success of such experiments in synthesizing living matter should not be interpreted, quite as much as they may be reckoned as confirming the hypothesis of a natural origin of life, as an implied rejection of the theory of a chance origin, even when this is reinforced by the usual considerations of the effects of the laws of probability over the immense periods of geological time before the appearance of life. The success of experiments in making life should raise no difficulties of principle (philosophical or theological) for the believer, the more so if his intellectual frame of reference is of the traditional Thomist kind.

CHAPTER III

THE CLASSIFICATION OF LIVING THINGS

For the proper understanding of the problems of biological evolution, one should know as accurately as possible the meanings of certain terms used by older and modern zoologists. Among these terms some represent *categories* by means of which is established the natural or artificial classification of living things. Let us introduce this question by quoting from W. J. Dakin's *Elements of General Zoology*[1]:

If we try to sort out all the animals known to us, we find that on the one hand the *mammals* (animals which suckle their young with milk—e.g. men, monkeys, cats, dogs, elephants, horses, sheep, etc.), the *birds*, the *reptiles* (snakes, lizards and crocodiles), *amphibia* (frogs and newts), and *fishes* all have a backbone, whilst the other groups of animals (sponges, jellyfish, insects, worms, etc.) lack this structure and other features that go with it. Therefore we group all the backboned animals into a big division called a phylum, and we name this the *vertebrata*. Within this phylum we recognize a series of groups called classes (mammals, birds, reptiles, amphibia and fishes). The cat belongs to the class *mammalia*. Within the class mammalia it is possible to distinguish another series of subdivisions. The cat, tiger, lion, bear, jackal and others have teeth adapted for a carnivorous diet. They agree in certain structural characters, and may be contrasted as a group to the hoofed animals like the pig, sheep,

[1] Oxford and New York, Oxford Univ. Press, 1928.

deer, oxen, etc., which are vegetarian. These divisions are known as orders, and the cat and its allies belong to the order *carnivora*. Other orders of the class mammalia are the *ungulata* (hoofed animals), the *rodentia* (beaver, rat, mouse, rabbit), the *marsupialia* (kangaroos), and there are several others. The order is further subdivided before we reach the genus. In the carnivora certain genera bear greater resemblances to one another, that is, seem more closely related than others. Thus the dogs, wolves and foxes resemble each other more closely than they resemble the cats, and the bears are different from both. These groups form the families *Canidae*, *Felidae*, and *Ursidae*. Finally the families are made up of the different genera, each composed of one or more species. We may thus tabulate the position of the cat as follows:

Kingdom	Animal
Phylum	Chordata (Vertebrata)
Class	Mammalia
Order	Carnivora
Family	Felidae
Genus	Felis
Species	Domesticus.[2]

Analogous examples could be given for plants. The existence of distinct groups is thus a "universal fact which might be considered as a fundamental characteristic of the diversity of organic life" (Dobzhansky). We may usefully add a few complementary notes to this.

SPECIES

Let us quote Littré's definition of species, which is still valid: "A collection of individuals descended from progenitors living or once alive, which have a greater resemblance to one another than to all other similar organisms, and which are able to reproduce themselves in a continuous manner, either together or in isolation, according to whether the sexes are united in one individual,[3] separate, or do not exist".[4] Two points in this

[2] *Op. cit.*, p. 4.
[3] As in plants and hermaphroditic animals.
[4] As in asexual organisms (reproduction by fission) or in reproduction by budding.

definition should be noted: the morphological resemblance of individuals, and their capacity to reproduce themselves, which they cannot do in union with individuals of other species. From these first suggestions it can be seen that the concept of species —at least when we are dealing with what the botanists and zoologists call "good" species*—corresponds to a concrete reality which can and ought to serve as an essential standard unit when for teaching or theoretical purposes a classification needs to be set up.

Since the work of the botanist A. Jordan (1814–97) species have been distinguished into elementary (*jordanons*) and collective or major (*linneons*), ideas which have been made precise in this century by genetics. Today, a jordanon is interpreted as a collection of individuals of pure race, in the sense that their gametes, or sex cells, completely correspond, in that they contain the same genes, the genes being the material factors of hereditary characteristics. By the conjunction of these gametes the *germ* is brought into being (the fertilized ovum or zygote) each exactly like the other, with the result that they are called homozygotes. In their development these germs give rise to a homogeneous population. From the same genetic viewpoint the linneon is seen to be a group of jordanons differing from one another in small characteristics. The individuals that make up the linneon are heterozygotes, because the gametes that come together at the moment of fertilization do not exactly correspond in their genetic make-up. By experimental intercrossing homozygote individuals can be obtained again, which when crossed will give perfectly stable types. "Thus the crucifer *Draba* (*Erophila*) *verna* L., with over two hundred elementary species, of which it is possible to find as many as a dozen growing within an area of a few square yards, includes forms which are apogamous and others which are hermaphrodite and cleistogamous. Artificial crossing of the latter may give fertile hybrids which produce apogamous types from which new pure lines can be cultured."[5]

[5] Lancelot Hogben, in *The New Systematics*, ed. Julian Huxley, Oxford Univ. Press, 1940, p. 276.

CLASSIFICATION ABOVE THE LEVEL OF SPECIES

Classification supposes the idea of a hierarchic order of living species, the hierarchy being based on the greater or less complexity of morphological and functional characteristics. It is in this way that animals are often described as "higher" or "lower". Now species resemble one another in different degrees, which justifies their being grouped into categories in which the common characteristics are progressively fewer but more fundamental. Briefly, systematics or taxonomy is the product of an abstractive process. This abstraction produces intellectual entities based on reality, but the most concrete reality above the level of the individual is always the species. Above that the taxonomist distinguishes the following principal categories:

Genus, a collection of species possessing one or more essential common characteristics: for example, the species or sub-genera panther, leopard, lion, tiger and jaguar, form the genus *panthera*.

The *family* is a group made up of several genera having some common characteristics: e.g., the family of the *Felidae* includes, as well as the cats already named, those of the genus *felis*, e.g. the ocelot, the puma, and the domestic cat, and the cheetah, of the genus *acinonyx*.

Above the family is the *order*, which is a collection of families having some fundamental characteristics in common. So, the order *Carnivora* includes as well as the Felidae nine other extant families: Canidae (dog, wolf, fox, jackal, etc.); Ursidae (bears); Procyonidae (raccoon, kinkajou, panda, etc.); Mustelidae (weasel, otter, badger, skunk, etc.); Viverridae (genet, civet, mongoose); Hyaenidae (aard-wolf, hyaena); Otariidae (sea-lions and fur seals); Odobenidae (walrus); and Phocidae (seals).

The union of several orders on the basis of similarity of essential characteristics is a *class*. There are, for example, six classes of vertebrates: Cyclostomes, Fish, Amphibians, Reptiles, Birds and Mammals.

The term *branch*, used in biology, is Cuvier's, who used the image of the division of the trunk of a tree into several branches. Three branches are distinguished in botany: Cryptogams, Monocotyledons and Dicotyledons; and usually nine in zoology: Protozoa, Coelenterates, Echinoderms, Worms, Arthropods, Molluscoids, Molluscs, Tunicates and Vertebrates.

VOCABULARY VARIANTS

Phyla

The phylum corresponds in use more or less to the branch of the older taxonomist. In evolutionary terminology, the phyla are evolutionary series, lines (in the genealogical sense of the word). Phylogeny is the study of the development of species from phyla; the word is used in contrast to ontogeny, which studies the embryological development of individuals. Teilhard de Chardin[6] considers the phylum to be "a collective reality", which "can be as small as one species or as large as a branch"; it is "a dynamic, natural reality: hence it can only appear with some dimension of duration, that is, in movement". The phylum is not "a superfluous artificial entity, isolated and cut off because it is needed for classifying in the living continuum. Looked at closely and in the proper light it is seen on the contrary as a perfectly determined structural reality." The phylum is classed among the *natural units* of the world because of "its own particular law and power of autonomous development". Despite the way of expressing it, it is not wholly metaphorical to say that it behaves like a living thing: it grows and blossoms out.

As it grows it tends to split into secondary phyla, each corresponding to a variant (or harmonic) of the fundamental type. It splits in some way along the front on which it is growing. Qualitatively it is subdivided just as, quantitatively, it spreads out. This is a split which recommences.[7] Sometimes the

---

[6] *Le Phénomène humain*, p. 121–2.
[7] Which supposes that the first split must be looked for in the roots of the tree of life.

new subdivisions seem not to correspond to any but superficial diversifications—the effects of chance or exuberant fantasy. Sometimes on the other hand they represent precise accommodation of the general type to particular needs or habitats. As is only to be expected this mechanism tends to repeat itself, in a finer degree, within the new subdivisions, which in their turn soon show signs of splitting further, so that the whole seems to open out fanwise. And theoretically the process is endless. In fact experience shows that the phenomenon dies away quickly: the opening of the fan soon stops, and the spread ends of the branches continue to grow without further appreciable division. The most general aspect presented by a fully developed and spread-out phylum is that of a verticil or whorl of well-established forms. . . .

At its beginning the phylum corresponds to the discovery by trial and error of a new organic type, viable and advantageous. But this type does not attain its most economic and best-adapted form straight away. For a longish time it uses all its power to feel its way forward, its attempts to improve itself follow one another without yet being definitively accepted, and then, perfection is nearly achieved: from that moment the rhythm of the change slows down, and new invention, come to the limits of its powers, enters its conquering phase. Stronger than its less perfect neighbours, the new-formed group spreads at the same time as it establishes itself and settles down: it enters at once its maximum both of growth and of stability. (Page 124.)

Cladi

Professor L. Cuénot, in his picture of the genealogical tree of the animal kingdom,[8] grants the existence of autonomous and closed "natural" groups:

I should compare these independent groups to leaves attached to the same stem: in the same way as one leaf of a tree is not derived from another leaf, it is impossible to make one existing type of structure proceed from another existing type. Since we cannot allow that these autonomous groups resulted from as many separate creative acts, they must be linked together, like leaves, at their (unknown) bases. What name can be given to

[8] *L'Évolution biologique,* pp. 16–18.

these autonomous "leaves"? To the terms already used—branch or phylum—which would suit admirably, I should prefer the word *cladus* (Gk. *klados*, a shoot or branch). If a cladus is rich in species it can be divided internally into genera, tribes, families, orders and classes. This subdivision can be represented as a small genealogical tree enclosed within the limits of the cladus, like the veins branching in a leaf.

These different passages are bound to raise various questions in the reader's mind, but we shall defer their consideration to the critical part of this book, until after the general lines of evolutionary theory have been presented.

ORGANIZATIONAL AND FORMAL TYPES

At this point it seems important to say something of the noteworthy distinction drawn by L. Vialleton thirty years ago between organizational and formal types[9]:

The various categories of classification can be separated into two groups, based on essentially different criteria: organization and form. The broad divisions from phylum to order, and their subdivisions, are solely based on organization, and the types which correspond to them are *organizational types*.[10] Below the level of order the criterion is no longer the same—the sign of the series changes, as it were. Organization is no longer relevant, for it remains the same for all the species of a single order. But these species are surely not a confused and chaotic jumble. They can be arranged naturally into a certain number of forms corresponding to actual families or the genera of the older naturalists, and these are *formal* or *specific types*.[11] The incredible profusion of living things in the world enforces the division of formal types into new categories, genera and species. But if these divisions are necessary in order to classify the numberless specimens of some groups they are nevertheless far from having the same value as the category above them, and

[9] *L'Origine des êtres vivants. L'illusion transformiste*, Paris, Plon, 1929, p. 175.
[10] Which Cuénot and others call structural types.
[11] Vialleton rejected the adjective "specific" because of the too narrow sense it has in present nomenclature.

only represent variants of formal types, particular adaptations to different conditions of time, place or environment; they are, in short, accidents of formal types.

Let us try to make these remarks more concrete by linking them with observed reality, and let us take as our example the phylum of vertebrates. It is divided into six classes: 1. Cyclostomes (without a lower jaw); 2. Fish; 3. Amphibia; 4. Reptiles; 5. Birds; 6. Mammals. Each of these is subdivided into orders, and it may be also, sub-orders. Let us take the mammals: the class divides into three sub-classes: 1. Prototheria or Monotremata (the platypus and spiny anteater); 2. Metatheria or Marsupials; 3. Eutheria. The last is richest in representatives, dividing into sixteen orders: Insectivores (e.g. hedgehog); Dermoptera (flying lemur); Cheiroptera (bats); Primates; Edentata (anteaters); Pholidota (scaly anteaters); Lagomorpha (e.g. rabbit); Rodents; Cetacea (whale, etc.); Carnivores; Tubulidentata (aardvark); Proboscidea (elephant, etc.); Hyracoidea (hyrax); Sirenia (sea-cow); Perissodactyla (e.g. horse, rhinoceros); Artiodactyla (e.g. pig, sheep). At this stage in classification comes the division which Vialleton proposes, between the higher and lower systematic groupings, phyla, classes and orders on the one hand and family, genus and species on the other. What kind of division is this? To answer this compare the definition of the class mammalia with that of one species of mammal. It is immediately obvious that the class is not a concrete object perceived by the senses but a generalized idea, a concept formed by abstraction from the direct perception of many objects possessing common characteristics. The thousands of species making up the class of mammals all have in common, besides those characteristics common to all vertebrates, certain fundamental characteristics, of which we select three for mention out of dozens of others: homoeothermic* blood, the presence of hair and the feeding of young with milk from mammary glands. By joining these characteristics to the others in thought we form the ideal mammal, which does not exist and has never existed in nature. This *noumenon*, Mammal, is an organizational type, a model, a mental construction out of elements taken from the sensible, physical world.

Organizational types—phyla, classes, orders—which form the higher categories of systematics make up the general plan of the living world as we are trying to reconstruct it. In reality, these ideal beings are realized by formal types; that is, by "beings which share with others at the same time in a common organization of proportions and structural details, a common form, in brief, which is proper to them and gives them, with a determinate place in the whole, a particular mode of action and a way of living."[12] "The first three categories (phylum, class, order) correspond to general ideas, and cannot be observed as such: there are in nature no phyla, classes or orders beside the species which possess their characteristics".[13] Let us call by their usual name a few formal types known to everyone, e.g. horse, dog; everyone recognizes a horse or a dog straight away. They belong to the class mammalia, to the sub-class eutheria. The horse belongs to the order perissodactyla and is a member of the single genus *equus* of the family of *equidae*, which contains six species. The dog belongs to the order carnivora, and to the family of canidae of which it is the type. The formal types found in reality in the horse or the dog are implied by organizational types, from phylum to order, and correspond, depending on the case chosen, to families, genera, species and races. It appears that the phenomena of adaptation and variation operate on the level of formal types, which are as it were spread out horizontally beneath what may be called the vertical hierarchy of organizational types. The same idea may be expressed by saying that the characteristics considered at the level of organizational types and those considered at formal-type level have different values. The living creature as we see it in nature has certain general characters which are essential and can be called primary. These are somehow masked by the much more numerous secondary characters,

[12] Vialleton, *op. cit.*, p. 200.
[13] *Ibid.*, p. 368.

infinitely more varied and variable. We shall later take these distinctions into account, for I think they ought to be kept in mind in a critical study of evolutionary theory. In fact, we shall see that the current concepts of micro-, macro- and mega-evolution, whether they be accepted or disputed, proceed from Vialleton's work.

CHAPTER IV

OUTLINE OF BIOLOGICAL

EVOLUTION

It is fairly common practice to push back the history of the idea of evolution to the beginning of the nineteenth century, to the publication in 1809 of Lamarck's *Zoological Philosophy* (trans. Hugh Elliott, London, 1914), followed by his *History of the Invertebrates* (1815–22). But this famous naturalist, born in 1744, was both in date and in ideas an eighteenth-century man, and the evolutionist argument can be regarded as beginning in the middle of the Age of Enlightenment with the work of Diderot and Buffon. But the works of Lamarck not only introduced the idea, new at that time, of the transformation of living species into others by the mechanism of heredity and external factors, but above all signified the freeing of the naturalist from the static philosophy which Linné (1707–78) had summed up in the famous phrase, *species tot sunt quot diversas formas ab initio produxit Infinitum Ens*—there are as many species as there are forms the Infinite Being created in the beginning. One may say that from Lamarck onwards the theory of evolution includes the two principles still appealed to today: the natural origin of life and the development of species from common stems—still appealed to irrespective of the various explanations that have been put forward. But it was equally from Lamarck onwards that the split between positive science and traditional metaphysics gradually widened and deepened, with the result that the natural sciences eliminated everything not consonant with material causation. This often leads natural scientists to materialist or mechanistic ideas. We shall see later that this attitude of mind, which has borne such abundant fruit in the last fifty years, very often contains implicitly a negative metaphysics, which may be admitted or not but which takes us back to the very beginnings of western thought. It is in fact odd that the most ancient Greek philosophers, the Ionians, and especially Heraclitus, the philosopher of Becoming, professed a doctrine which, wanting to explain all phenomena by a single principle, logically ended in monism and pantheism. In fact modern evolutionary theory since Lamarck, which could perhaps have developed in a purely scientific atmosphere by limiting itself to the realm of sensible objects, has never remained independent of metaphysical presuppositions and conclusions. So much so that cosmological theories have been described as fairy-tales woven around the observed facts.

The principal argument supporting the theory of evolution is paradoxically Cuvier's palaeontological vision of the succession in time of more and more perfect living things, of which man would prove to be the most recent if not the last example. This picture is coherent and consistent if we ignore certain difficulties which have still not yet been settled and which will be examined later. In general, taking into account the palaeontological discoveries of the time since the beginnings of evolutionary speculation, the old classifications (static) cover also the new ones (evolutionary), which are presented in the form of a genealogical tree with roots, trunk, boughs, branches and leaves. Both classifications admit of a succession in time of vegetable and animal forms together with the perfecting of some of them. But pre-evolutionary classifications, as we have already noted, admit discontinuities in the story of living things, which led the first palaeontologists like Cuvier and d'Orbigny to claim that there were successive creations separated by violent geological cataclysms. What is more, this idea of a relationship between taxonomic discontinuities and geological phenomena is still held. G. G. Simpson, for example, expresses himself in this way: "There probably is some real coincidence between tectonic episodes and the rise of new taxonomic groups on the mega-evolutionary level, especially as regards terrestrial animals (or sequences beginning or ending in such), a significant point. For instance, the orders of the four classes of 'fishes' and of the class Amphibia show no more probable coincidence of time of origin with times of orogeny than could be due to chance alone, but among reptiles and mammals the proportion of orders that seem to have arisen during times of pronounced emergence and orogeny is greater than can reasonably be ascribed to chance."[1] But even here it is the idea of genealogical continuity or descent which guides the great majority of present-day biologists, whether they are palaeontologists, who decipher the record of the rocks, or neontologists, who study present living material. In the critical part of this book we shall consider the conflict between this idea of the genealogical continuity of all living things and the discontinuity of species as they are, which is recognized by all contemporary biologists. But first of all let us see what general picture of evolution emerges.

GENERAL OUTLINE OF EVOLUTIONARY THEORY [2]

The first creatures to appear on our planet have left no important traces because of the geological phenomenon of the metamorphosis of the rocks. Fossils of the pre-Cambrian era are so far of dubious authenticity. In the Cambrian deposits which seem to be about five hundred million years old, we find invertebrates of all the important phyla, but the vertebrates do not appear until later, in the Ordovician. In a general way

[1] G. G. Simpson, *Tempo and Mode in Evolution*, Columbia University Press, 1944, p. 113.

[2] We do not need to set out over again the various classical "proofs" of evolution (anatomical, palaeontological, embryological, ecological and so on) which can be found in general works and textbooks. We shall merely remark that the "fact" of evolution, in the minds of most of our contemporaries, results from the conjunction of a methodological assumption (see for example L. von Bertalanffy, "The Present State of the Problem of Evolution", *Scientia*, Milan, 1929) and the increasing complexity observed in the story of life.

palaeontology shows that evolution is progressive in the sense that living things present more complicated morphological and functional features the more recent the geological strata containing their fossils. A complete picture of evolution would have to include Protista, plants and animals. Within the limits of a book of this kind, the aim of which is to set man in his place among living species, we must restrict ourselves to categories narrower than the animal kingdom—narrower even than the phylum of vertebrates—to the class of mammals, the order of primates, etc. In this chapter we shall only consider the members and the connections of the class of mammals, as a subdivision of the phylum of vertebrates, and shall reserve a special chapter for the appearance of man.

The first vertebrates of which we have any knowledge are the cyclostomes or agnatha (aquatic animals of the same kind as lampreys, with a round and jawless mouth) which appeared in the Ordovician era. They are followed by the fishes, and in the Silurian by the now extinct placodermata. From these in the Devonian came the cartilaginous and bony fishes. Later in the Devonian the amphibians came from the bony fishes, and from the amphibia in the late Carboniferous the reptiles. Lastly, from the reptiles came, in the upper Triassic, the mammals, and the birds not until the Jurassic. The reptiles reached their evolutionary peak in the Secondary period, the mammals theirs in the Tertiary, yet there still exist alongside the many different kinds of mammals a reptilian fauna still important despite its reduction. Present-day reptiles are, from one point of view, more evolved than the extinct reptiles of the Secondary period, but they are fundamentally less developed than mammals. As a result of this persistence of forms that have, in a sense, been left behind, the sense of progressive development which seems implicit in the palaeontological facts is confirmed by the study of forms as they now are, which reveal various levels of organization corresponding to complex genealogical trees developed over a long time. This summary can be tabulated as follows (the figures showing the time in millions of years from the epoch named to the present):

Primary (Palaeozoic)	Cyclostomes	.	.	420	Ordovician
	Fishes	.	.	355	Silurian
	Cartilaginous fishes	.		325	Devonian
	Bony fishes	.	.	325	
	Amphibia	.	.	325	Late Devonian
	Reptiles	.	.	285	Late Carboniferous
Secondary (Mesozoic)	Mammals	.	.	200	Upper Triassic
	Birds	.	.	175	Jurassic

Palaeontologists put the original vertebrates into the phylum *Chordata*, so called because its members possess a dorsal cord for some or all of their lives. The phylum of chordates is subdivided into three sub-phyla, urochordata, cephalochordata, and notochordata or vertebrates. The first is represented by the Ascidians in which the "cord" is generally present only in one stage of life; the second by Amphioxus, in which the cord goes from one end of the body to the other; and the vertebrates have a cord which does not quite reach the end of the body at the head end and which in the adult is more or less completely replaced by a vertebral column. Some writers have made Amphioxus the ancestor of the vertebrates, because it combines invertebrate characters with the essential marks of the vertebrates, but there are some doubts about this. Amphioxus occupies a position at the bottom of the vertebrate scale similar to that of Peripatus at the bottom of the arthropods. Neither is at the bottom in terms of *origin*: they most likely represent small branches which were very early separated from the common stock, became specialized, and evolved very little in the course of time. They may show us what sort of creatures the original ancestors were, but more cannot be deduced from their study.

Living vertebrates are divided into seven classes. The first and most primitive is that of the cyclostomes, round-mouthed vertebrates, with no articulated jaw to limit the buccal orifice. Another primitive feature is the absence of paired appendages. The best known cyclostomes are the lampreys, anguilliform and living in the sea or in rivers. From this class are distinguished all the others, the gnathostomes, that is, with mouths with articulated jaws. These are divided into pinnipeds, with paired appendages in the form of fins, making up the two classes of cartilaginous and bony fishes; and tetrapods, with two pairs of locomotory appendages. The tetrapods include the Anamniotes and the Amniotes, the latter having and the former not having an amniotic sac* in the embryo. The amphibia alone belong to the first division, and their best known characteristic is the branchial respiration of the larval stage, succeeded by the pulmonary respiration after metamorphosis. Lastly the Amniotes include three classes, reptiles, birds and mammals. Reptiles and birds can be joined again in a super-class, the Sauropsidians, oviparous or, exceptionally, ovoviviparous. Reptiles are poikilothermic* and have scaly skins; birds are homoeothermic and have feathers, and forelimbs transformed into wings. Mammals are homoeothermic, have hair and mammary glands, and are generally viviparous, though the monotremes are oviparous. Mammals are usually divided into the monotremes, which are oviparous; the marsupials, which are viviparous but not placental; and the placental mammals, which include many orders and most of the present-day mammals (edentates, ungulates, sirenians, carnivores, rodents, cetacea, cheiroptera, insectivores, lemurs, and primates).

The batrachians are commonly supposed to have originated from fish of crossopterygian* type[3] through forms similar to the Devonian ichthyostegidae* of Greenland. These intermediary forms are unfortunately not known: no fossil form shows the transition from the paired fin to the characteristic tetrapod limb. Reptiles are derived from the amphibians, with intermediary forms recalling the cotylosaur* Seymouria of the Permian in Texas, the morphology of which belongs as much to that of the stegocephalian* amphibians as to that of the cotylosaurian reptiles among which it is generally classified. As for the mammals, the few and very small primitive forms which appear from the Triassic and Jurassic onwards must

[3] See for example G. S. Carter, *Animal Evolution* (London, 1951), p. 279.

have been similar to the ictidosaurians, theriodont* reptiles belonging to the great group of theromorphs.* These primitive mammalian forms, close in kind to the non-placental mammals, are sometimes grouped as allotheria. At last, in the Eocene, during which the great orders of Secondary reptiles disappeared, a whole series of various mammalian faunas occurs, roughly sketching out the different orders now known and including in particular incontestable placental types.

MONOPHYLETISM AND POLYPHYLETISM

The successive appearances presented by the world of life during past ages, the astounding unfolding of which palaeontology since Cuvier has retraced with ever-increasing accuracy of detail, can be interpreted by evolutionists in two ways, monophyletically or polyphyletically. Haeckel (1866) followed Lamarck's earlier scheme in postulating the descent of all living things, vegetable and animal, from a primitive *monas*, and his genealogical tree of life is consequently monophyletic and supposes the following succession in time for the animal kingdom: protozoa, invertebrate metazoa, vertebrates, mammals. For Erlsberg, on the other hand, followed by numerous others, evolution begins from a number of independent branches, from several phyla each evolving on its own account; that is, evolution is polyphyletic. This idea has now prevailed over the monophyletic, but scientists are not yet agreed on the number of primitive phyla or divisions. Some tend to make the number small, others make it large. The monophyletic theory, which succeeds in a certain economy of improbability when the origins of life are in question, raises the difficult problem of the relations between the higher groups, for which a solution has not yet been found, as we shall see later. On the other hand the polyphyletic theory evades this problem but requires as a hypothesis for the origins of life a number of primitive organisms, the number being equal to the number of phyla presumed to be irreducible to any other. By multiplying the number of phyla supposed to be independent a limit is reached; thus a hypothesis is set up, in place of

Cuvier's idea of successive creations, that the appearance of life on earth may have included at once and together the seeds of all possible sexual and asexual forms or of certain root forms. Some of these multiplied and proliferated at once, others would have been kept in reserve in dormant forms.

RULES AND METHODS OF EVOLUTION

Evolutionary laws

It is possible to extract from the palaeontologist's list of phenotypes* which have succeeded one another in the course of the evolution of life a number of "laws", or more exactly "rules", of varying validity, but corresponding to fairly general precepts. From among these laws, to use the usual term, which have the merit above all of furnishing a synthetic description of palaeontological data, let us note the following:

Law of increasing complexity: the evolution of living things, from the point of view of the appearance of the great structural types, proceeds from the simple to the complex; that is, in a (taxonomically and morphologically) progressive sense.

Law of progressive speciation of phyletic branches: phyletic evolution generally moves towards the establishment of types more and more distinct and specialized.

Law of increasing size: in the course of phyletic evolution there is a growth in the size of the organism from the small forms at the beginning of each division to the giant forms at its end.

Law of adaptive radiation: a period of rapid diversification or of "adaptive radiation" generally follows that of the differentiation of the phyla, marked by the appearance of a series of progressively more specific branches.

Law of migrations: the evolution of phyla often includes important migrations connected with certain palaeogeographic changes.

Law of substitution: the broad types of organization seem to take the place of one another in the course of time, after a phase of maximum development followed by one of regression.

Law of non-specialization of root forms: only those organic types which are not specialized are susceptible of further evolution, these types being generally of small size and few in number.

Law of irreversibility (Dollo's law): regressive evolution (e.g., disappearance of a group, atrophy of an organ, diminution in size) is irreversible. In its earlier formulation, the irreversibility of evolution was associated with its limited and discontinuous character; in the later (Cuénot's "regressive and irreversible orthogenesis") it is restricted, as we have here stated it, to regressive changes.

Some writers have proposed a "law of evolutionary continuity", according to which the ends of an evolutionary series would be linked by a continuous series of intermediaries without any observable breaks or jumps. This "law" (which flatly contradicts one of the fundamental assumptions of Dollo, of discontinuity, and even also that of limitations) is valid for some series which are continuous but exceptional (Slavonic fresh-water gastropods, for example, or irregular sea-urchins of *Micraster* type). It could without raising great difficulties be extended to many well-known and limited orthogenetic series, such as are found for example within the orders in some vertebrate classes (the classic series of *equidae*, etc.). But this "law" is not (for the time being?) acceptable when we are concerned with the larger groupings (phyla, etc.) which seem to be quite distinct even at the level of their first known representatives; distinct, very ancient, and possessing characters such that the hypothesis that there are intermediate forms is untenable.

These various laws which we have just listed are thought of by some as laws of "orthogenesis", either progressive (law of specialization) or regressive (Dollo's law). We shall see later how we can put a more restrictive interpretation on this very general conception of orthogenesis, taken to express, fundamentally, the "normal", orientated character of evolutionary phyletic changes, at least as these appear as the result of either hypothetical factors of selection or of the "drift" of assemblages of genotypes.*

Evolutionary rates

So far as they can be discovered by palaeontology (for example, by the relation between the magnitude of some phenotypic changes and the time needed for them to have shown themselves) these are extremely variable. In some phyla the rate is nearly zero (Simpson's bradytelic types) and sometimes it is appreciable or even very high (Simpson's tachytelic types), although it is still most often impossible to grasp the exact causes.

Micro-, macro- and mega-evolution

The methodological necessity to take account of the teachings of palaeontology concerning the development of life has of course led biologists to admit several distinct methods in the evolutionary process itself, even though some of them hope to reduce these methods some day to a single mechanism. We shall come back to this point of view later, but it is possible now to distinguish evolution of a continuous kind, small in its effects, limited to the lower systematic divisions such as sub-species, species, or even genera (*micro-evolution*, or "slow variation"); evolution on a larger scale, but still continuous, and showing a progressive drift on the whole, limited to the middle groupings such as genera and families (*macro-evolution*, or phyletic evolution); and lastly evolution of a quantum or discontinuous kind, usually pre-adaptive and concerning the higher systematic groupings such as families, orders and above (*mega-evolution*, quantum evolution, or "lateral variation"). We shall return to these questions in the chapters on the explanatory hypotheses of evolution and on the scientific difficulties of general evolutionary theory.

CHAPTER V

ANTHROPOGENESIS: THE ORIGINS OF MAN FROM THE EVOLUTIONARY STANDPOINT

It should have been possible to keep the problem of the origins of man limited to the purely scientific level. But since the beginnings of evolutionary ideas it has been tied up with a series of philosophical and anti-religious views, some of which cannot but create an unfortunate polemical atmosphere productive of excesses and confusion. The story of *Eoanthropus Dawsoni*, discovered by Charles Dawson at Piltdown between 1908 and 1915, will illustrate the prejudice with which some men, happily very few, approach the question of human beginnings. The chief interest in this discovery, which was studied by a number of palaeontologists, and in particular by Smith Woodward, lay in its site, which was dated to the lower pleistocene (upper palaeolithic), for this made it older than Neanderthal man. Secondly, the cranium of this "hominid" showed no differences from that of *Homo sapiens*, although the jaw and teeth possessed unmistakably pithecoid characters. A controversy arose in which men with great qualifications, like Sir Arthur Smith Woodward, Sir Arthur Keith and Eliot Smith, took part. The use of modern techniques (the quantitative analysis of fluorine and nitrogen content, etc.) on these "ancient" relics compels the conclusion that the cranium of Eoanthropus was relatively recent, and the jaw more recent still, being that of an ape, cleverly faked with a file, after the teeth had been extracted—all without the knowledge of those who were later to study it anatomically.[1]

At the present day, even if we cannot say that all metaphysical motives—or even some political ones—have quite gone from some men's minds, we can agree with some satisfaction that the argument is now conducted in a more peaceful atmosphere and with a real regard for objectivity. It is true that agreement has not been reached as between the different genealogies which can all be supported in different ways by the evidence of the palaeontological record, which is common to all, but still insufficient. Nevertheless a certain convergence of views is appearing, in which the human family appears more and more to many evolutionists as constituting a privileged "axis", or even the major axis, of all biological evolution.

THE PLACE OF MAN IN NATURE

For the zoologist, man belongs to the *order* of primates; this belongs to the vertebrate *phylum*, through the intermediate steps of *class*, mammalia and *sub-class*, placental animals. The order of primates is subdivided into two sub-orders, the Prosimii and the Anthropoidea. The latter is divided into three superfamilies, the Ceboidea (Platyrrhini), the New World monkeys; Cercopithecoidea, the Old World monkeys; and the Hominoidea. The last two make up the older superfamily of the Catarrhini. The Hominoidea contains two extant families, the Pongidae, or apes, and the Hominidae, true men, the fifth extant family of the Anthropoidea. Primates can be defined as pentadactyl, plantigrade mammals; with generally opposable thumbs and big toes; full and bunodont dentition (that is, teeth with separate cusps for grinding); orbit separated from the temporal fossa by a large vertical bony bar (except in the

[1] A full account of this forgery will be found in J. S. Weiner's *The Piltdown Forgery* (Oxford University Press, 1955).

lemurs); pectoral mammary glands (except in certain lemurs and the tarsiers); fully developed telencephalon which is generally circumvoluted and, except in lemurs, covers the cerebellum; free radius and ulna, etc. Man has the same general organization as the anthropomorphs but is distinguished in certain ways: some characters are derived from his upright stance—curved spine, enlarged pelvis, vertical upper and lower limbs, occipital condyle moved towards the centre of the base of the skull, etc.—and other differences are the astonishing development of the cerebral hemispheres, the reduction in the bones of the face, the wider facial angle, the development of a chin, the presence of canines not protruding above the other teeth, the absence of the central bone of the wrist, and a whole series of other characteristics which it would be wearisome to set out in detail. These characters taken together justify zoologists' placing man separately in a taxonomic division of his own on the level of the family or sub-family. And truly, as many writers marked a long time ago, what constitutes the essential distinction of man is not his organic make-up, which is not very different from that of other mammals, particularly the primates; what is characteristic is *human thought*. We shall have to return more than once to this very important fact, the significance of which should not be underestimated.

THE EVOLUTIONARY PROBLEM OF THE ORIGIN OF MAN

From the palaeontological record now known we can form the opinion that man can no longer be separated from the general succession of living things; in no way is he an exceptional being. The fact that for a long time, and still today by many people, man is put into a special category is due to ignorance of the natural order. Man takes his place naturally in the series of living things. But it is nevertheless not a question of putting man on a level with the animals: man does mark a new step in evolution. From the palaeontological traces of the chronological succession of phenotypes there follow:

(a) that there is a whole series of fossil forms intermediate between present men and certain root forms of some other groups of primates, the number of these intermediate forms growing as research progresses;

(b) that (almost all writers on this subject agree) there is no form transitional between man, present-day or fossil, and any representative of any other kind of primate today, including the simiids.

From the first of these two statements the evolutionist is bound to affirm a genetic (or hereditary) continuity between man today and certain pre-human fossil forms of primates (theory of the ascent of man from the brutes). If we leave aside provisionally, to help the argument, the problem of the ways man first evolved; that is, if we accept the hypothesis of the animal origin of man, considered as a biological object, we can set out as follows the series of forms strung out along the line of his evolution, though some of them may not be exactly in that line, but are only loose strands, as it were.

Paranthropoids, or para-hominids

Under this head can be grouped a collection of forms dating probably from the end of the pliocene (that is, the very end of the tertiary) to the beginning of the pleistocene (lower quaternary)—going back, that is, several hundred thousand years or perhaps even a million. They are represented essentially by the Australopithecines of various kinds (Australopithecus, Paranthropus, Plesianthropus, Telanthropus).

Anthropids, or pre-hominids

Existing from the lower to the middle pleistocene they include various forms (Pithecanthropus erectus, Sinanthropus pekinensis, Africanthropus niarasensis), to which may be added some transitional (?) types like Heidelberg man or Mauranthropus, which foreshadow the "flood" of primitive hominids that followed.

Hominids

The flood of hominids properly so called appears to consist of two waves: the first, *primitive*, *praesapiens* or *parasapiens*, of the middle pleistocene, characterized by the type Neanderthal man and neighbouring forms (*Homo palestinus*, *H. rhodesiensis*, *H. soloensis*) of different degrees of development, some of which (*H. rhodesiensis* and *H. soloensis*) are sometimes interpreted as representing end-products of allied lines of descent of the group of Australopithecus and Pithecanthropus respectively. The Saldanha skull discovered at Hopefield in 1951 perhaps belongs to *H. rhodesiensis* or *H. soloensis*. The second wave is *recent* (*sapiens*, properly so called) at the lower end of which are found in the middle of the pleistocene forms of *proto-sapiens* type (Steinheim, Swanscombe and Fontéchevade man), of comparable age with the typical Neanderthal man or even older, yet closer to the *sapiens* type. The well-known types of Brunn, Cro-Magnon, Chancelade and Grimaldi followed, the whole recent "wave" stretching from about thirty-five thousand years before our age to the holocene, our own time. Between these two dates must be placed the diversification of present races, which have the value of subspecies: Australoids, Negroids, Mongoloids and Europeoids.

THE PROBLEM OF THE (PALAEONTOLOGICAL) MODES OF MAN'S FIRST EVOLUTION

If we accept the evolutionary picture of man's origins, that is, if we accept the assertion that man is one group among the animals, the problem is raised of the ways in which man developed, a real problem so far as it is open to investigation by the palaeontological study of phenotypes. In practice this problem is reduced to two questions: was there one or were there many zoological roots of the human family and, what was the size (in terms of "population") of these roots? These are the ways man may have first evolved, thought of either as a "boundary" between forms separated by a generation, or as an "area" to pass over or through which took many successive generations.

The first question, whether there were many roots or one, seems now to have been answered by most writers in favour of monophyletism, the polyphyletic theory having only received much support a few decades ago. There are three monophyletic theories of man's origins. The first postulates the common origin, from an initial miocene dryopithecus,* of the orang-outan on one side and of man, gorilla and chimpanzee on the other. The gibbons, more primitive in their structure, must have split off before the dryopitheci appeared. The fundamental change that marked the apparition of the human line of descent must have been the transition from an arboreal life and a vegetable diet to a bipedal terrestrial life with an omnivorous diet and predatory habits. An adjustment of the proportions of the limbs, and the loss of the prehensibility and opposition of the big toe would have followed, and at the same time the change in diet would have caused the regression of man's facial structure and the dental arches, and the reduction of his canine teeth and jaw muscles.

The second theory pushes back the origin of man further than that of the anthropomorphs. The supporters of this idea disagree, however, on the point of origin, the lemuroids or the tarsioids. The latter would take the origin of the human family back to a very ancient epoch of the tertiary or even perhaps the end of the secondary. Though represented now by a single species, the tarsius of Malaya, the tarsioids had in the palaeocene and eocene a very wide distribution, and the existence in them of many primitive characteristics, some of which are intermediate between those of the lemuroids and the monkeys, has caused them sometimes to be regarded as the original group of all primates. From one of these first tarsioids the human line would very early have split off.

There are difficulties with both these theories which cannot be examined here, but a third has been proposed as a *tertium quid* as a result of the discovery in South Africa of the Australopithecus group of fossils. These creatures, as opposed to the anthropomorphs, stood upright. Now it is reasonable to suppose that if man and the australopithecines have or had an upright stance, this is because they had been somehow pre-disposed to it by a previous adaptation to an arboreal life. This is the property of the anthropomorphs, so we can con-clude that it is from these, at a time when they had already begun to live in trees, that the stock split off from which the australopithecines and man descended. Only, while among the true anthropomorphs the adaptation to an arboreal life simply increased to the point of extreme specialization, in the australo-pithecid-hominid group this adaptation took a sharp turn and only those characteristics proper to bipedal locomotion de-veloped. From the discovery of australopithecus we know now that the ability to walk on two feet and the concomitant freeing of the hand from all locomotive functions are early phenomena which appear before the beginnings of man. What brings man on to the scene is not his hand nor his bipedal gait but his cerebral development, which made possible two other, specific-ally human, characteristics: conscious reason and speech. From the moment when the brain attained a sufficient volume relative to that of the body as a whole, together with the differentiation of the essential psychic centres, the small-toothed australo-pithecus can be called man. This theory of the origin of man from an already bipedal anthropomorph stock certainly pre-sents the double advantage of being properly based on the palaeontological facts and of being in strict accord with the comparative anatomical and physiological data. In the present state of our knowledge it looks the most likely hypothesis.

Until very recently it had long been held that Asia, and especially south-east Asia, was the cradle of primitive man. Lately various indications, such as the discovery in Africa of a stone industry of pre-Chellean type (the pebble industry of Oldoway in Kenya) more primitive than that associated with the Sinanthropi, seem to show that Africa may well have been the birth-place of the primitive members of the species *Homo sapiens*, who must have split off very early from the family (*para*- and not *pre*-hominid) of australopithecines. "To explain the appearance, on the edges as it were of the australopithecines, of the pebble industry, we must suppose the emergence in

Africa at the beginning of the pleistocene of a first type, X, of man. Now to account for the subsequent sudden development in the same places of a flake industry producing bi-faced implements[2] we must postulate the formation in central and east Africa of a second wave of particularly progressive men (call them type Y) which, to judge from the Kanam jaw—admitting it to be genuinely ancient—may well represent the long-sought roots of the stock of *Homo sapiens* himself."[3]

Accepting the hypothesis, certainly and no doubt finally preferred by zoologists, of a monophyletic origin of the zoological family of man, the problem still remains of the size (in terms of "populations") of the original offshoot of this group arising from certain pre-hominid forms of the order of primates. There are two principal answers: polygeny, admitting a large number of hominids of the first generation, and monogeny, reducing these to a primitive pair. The idea of hologeny once offered as a third kind of answer in fact approximates to polygeny, with the addition of a fundamental assertion of a wide geographical dispersion of basic forms (dormant) of the first generation. We need not here discuss the eventual theological repercussions of one or other of these ideas, hologeny, polygeny, or monogeny; nor need we decide whether, as Teilhard de Chardin wrote a quarter of a century ago, "science left to itself would never dream (it is the least one may say) of suggesting a basis as narrow as two individuals for the enormous structure of the human race."[4] Let us simply remark that on the evolutionary hypothesis monogeny is the idea closest to a literal interpretation of the Bible. Although this is not *de fide*, polygeny can hardly be in accord with the revealed truths proposed to the faith of Catholics, nor is it authorized by ecclesiastical

[2] We are here concerned with African stone industries of Chellean and Acheulean types lying above the pebble industry, very old, abundant and varied, and known now over a vast region of central Africa.

[3] Teilhard de Chardin: "L'Afrique et les origines humaines", *Revue des questions scientifiques*, January 20th, 1955.

[4] Quoted by Fr Descoqs, S.J., in *Autour de la crise du transformisme*, p. 81; Paris, Beauchesne, 1944.

authority.[5] We ought to add to this that neither palaeontology
nor the knowledge acquired by contemporary zoology will be
able to confirm or refute one or other of the two hypotheses,
mono- or polygeny, nor even simply to make one clearly and
distinctly preferable to the other.

Modes of origin

It seems that very little can be said from the purely
palaeontological point of view on the problem of the specific
ways man originated; that is, the transition from animal to
man. Indeed, we have seen that the group *hominidae* is contained in a taxonomic division of middle, or even minor, rank
(according to some it is only of the order of a genus), and that
it is characterized by the persistence of a certain collection of
"primitive" or non-specialized characteristics (hence such
theories as that of foetalization of Bolk), which are moreover
associated with other characteristics considered "progressive".
On the other hand, the points of origin of these phyletic off-
shoots normally correspond to the blanks in the palaeontological record; the situation is aggravated by the methodological
consideration that resemblance does not necessarily indicate
descent, even when the chronological relations are perfectly
well-established.

If these two facts are considered together with a third, that
the appearance of man inaugurated a new stage in the story
of the earth or that of life, by the introduction of thought
("psychozoic era", "noösphere", etc.), then it would seem
scarcely reasonable to expect a truly enlightening explanation
of man's origins to come from the simple examination of the
series (even supposing it to be complete) of phenotypes linking
the zoological family *hominidae* to this or that long-extinct
group of primates. The only problem properly the province of
palaeontology is whether the transition from beast to man

[5] Encyclical of Pius XII, *Humani Generis*, 1950; English translation
"False Trends in Modern Teaching", London, Catholic Truth Society,
1957; § 37; see also *The Papal Encyclicals in their Historical Context*,
edited by Anne Fremantle, New York, New American Library, 1956,
p. 287.

should be thought of as a boundary or as an area; to put it another way, did it happen progressively or continuously, or suddenly, discontinuously? The continuity or discontinuity in question is in the succession of *phenotypes*, since the *genetic* continuity is, on the evolutionary view, presupposed. Still it must be said that granted the effects of the extreme distance in time of the changes under consideration, and the somewhat arbitrary nature of the scientific criteria of what would constitute a man as distinct from a pre-hominid type, a transition from animal to man which was really, historically, drawn out in time and phenotypically continuous would most likely appear to us discontinuous. What is more, such a process (orthogenetic) seems surely no more likely than an orthogenetic series of mutations of a certain size or even a unique "mega-mutation" causing the passing over of the boundary or area separating man from the animals; that is, separating the biosphere from the noösphere. Whether such a mega-mutation or series of mutations of varying sizes only represents the objective appearance or the phenomenal correlative of a change really and primarily (in the causal order) ontological, is a question we shall examine later.

CHAPTER VI

EXPLANATORY HYPOTHESES OF EVOLUTION

Since the beginnings of evolutionary ideas scientists have sought to make them respectable by appealing to various causal explanations. Many such theories have followed one another in history, and in a short survey we can reduce them to five: Lamarckism, Darwinism, mutation theory, the synthetic theory prevalent at present, and the theory of paedomorphosis.

LAMARCKISM

In his *Zoological Philosophy* (1809, English trans., 1914) Lamarck says that we are only presented by nature with *individuals* which succeed one another by descent, but that species are not unchanging but pass one into another. Their changes are effected by the influence of the environment; that is, by external factors. Let us recall Lamarck's two laws summarizing his ideas, and notice their simplicity:

First law: in any animal *which has not passed the limit of its development*, the more frequent and sustained use of any organ gradually strengthens that organ, develops and enlarges it, and gives it a power proportionate to the period of that usage; while the constant disuse of any organ insensibly weakens it, deteriorates it, progressively diminishes its faculties, and ends by causing it to disappear.

Second law: all characteristics which nature has caused individuals to acquire or lose by the influence of the circumstances
to which their kind has for a long time been subjected, and
consequently by the influence of the predominant usage of any
organ or that of the constant disuse of any part, are preserved
by inheritance in new individuals which are born of them, provided the acquired changes are common to both sexes or belong
to those which produce the new individuals.

These laws are open to two major criticisms. So far as concerns the effects of the environment, it is well-known that
certain external factors such as light, temperature, atmospheric
pressure, salinity, etc., have some influence on an organism,
but the changes they produce are of two kinds: sometimes they
belong to the class of functional regulating changes which are
characteristic of life, and they can be called "auto-adaptive
variations"; sometimes they are apparently random and insignificant for the individual ("indeterminate non-adaptive
variations"). These latter clearly have less interest from the
point of view of the evolutionary explanation of "established
adaptations". Again, so far as concerns the inheritance of the
variations acquired under the influence of the normal behaviour of an organism or the environment, all experiments
performed so far have yielded negative results. It all happens
as if variations were incapable of modifying the specific genetic
inheritance and only ever concerned the one *soma* (Gk. "body");
hence the name *somation* given to them by Plate or "accommodation" proposed by Cuénot. True, appeal can be made, in
order to lessen the effect of these results, to certain observed
inherited organic arrangements (the sternal or pubic callosities
of the ostrich, the callosities of the wart-hog, etc.), which oddly
mimic various accommodations which are the result of use.
Above all, the objection can be made, as we shall see later,
that the experiments have had far too short a time compared
with the immensities of geological time; and also that present
organisms may have reached a stable state less modifiable than
that in their earlier history. In any case, even if a definitive
judgement cannot yet be given on Lamarckism, it must be

recognized that for very good theoretical and experimental reasons we must reject the central hypothesis of the Lamarckian theory, namely, the idea of the inheritance of characteristics acquired by a particular *soma*.

DARWINISM

In his book *The Origin of Species* (1859) Charles Darwin made known the fruit of twenty years' thought on the subject, with considerable documentation, notably that which he had accumulated in the course of his round-the-world trip in the *Beagle* (1831–6). He proposed, half a century after Lamarck, a demonstration with considerable precise evidence of the facts of biological evolution, together with an explanation of these facts which was to have considerable repercussions. In particular he thought that, on the basis of the observations he had been able to make on his world cruise and of his experience of the changes of race deliberately obtained by breeders, he could account for the basic assertion of evolution (namely, the "family relationship" of species and higher groups) by the interplay of on the one hand the spontaneous *variability* of creatures and their *reproductive powers*, and on the other the *struggle for existence* which followed the exercise of these powers, the result of which is a *selection* (Lat. *seligere*, to pick out) with an overall elimination of ill-adapted types and the survival of more adapted ones. One of the principal marks, and for some minds principal advantages, of Darwin's ideas was clearly that they ascribed or "seemed to ascribe the production of new species of organisms to the operation of purely natural forces working haphazardly. No inner urge, no propelling force, was necessary to account for the change of species in the living world."[1] So much is this so that at the beginning of this century a prospectus offering a one-volume French edition of *The Origin of Species* called the book an "immortal one which finally demolished the Biblical story of the creation and revealed the scientific laws of evolution, so that a new scientific

[1] P. G. Fothergill, *Historical Aspects of Evolution* (London, 1952), p. 118.

era began from the date of its first publication". As we shall
see later this aspect is always considered a merit by the supporters of a synthetic theory of evolution.

We shall not examine here certain ideas added to the notion
of evolution just described either by Darwin himself (sexual
selection) or by his immediate successors such as Weismann[2]
(theory of the continuity of the germ plasm; non-inheritance of
acquired characteristics; genetic selection, etc.), and we shall
content ourselves with listing a number of criticisms which
limit the explanatory value of Darwin's ideas a good deal.

(a) Most individual genetic variations ("sports") are small
and seem to offer little for the mechanism of natural selection
to work on.

(b) The struggle for existence has neither the generality nor
the consequences Darwin supposed. Its ultimate sanction,
death, can only advance the natural end of existence, and that
in ways such that it seems less the developer of differences than
the conserver of the normal specific type.

(c) Natural selection (is there any need to state explicitly
that there is absolutely no question of a "cause" with intrinsic
morphogenetic powers?) cannot properly be compared with
artificial selection, since the latter, by deliberate and intelligent
choice of crosses, by preventing some unions taking place, and
by manipulating the environment, introduces precisely the
purposive factor that Darwinism denies in natural processes.
The study of domestic animals which have returned to the
wild life is enough to show that natural selection even has the
opposite effect, namely the elimination of variants.

(d) Finally, even had natural selection the efficacy of artificial selection its influence would automatically cease with the
realization of a homozygote genotype.

MUTATION THEORY

The mutation theory was first formulated by the Dutch
botanist Hugo de Vries in his *Mutation Theory* (1901, English

[2] It would be of great interest though too lengthy to set out the details of Weismann's conceptions, the effects of which on biology in
general are still considerable.

trans., 1910), after a long series of investigations, from 1886–1901, made on Œnothera Lamarckiana (the Evening Primrose), of the family of the Onagraria (from the Latin *onager*, "an ass", the plants of the genus Œnothera being supposed to provide a rich pasturage for these animals) or Œnotherea, the genus Œnothera having a hundred odd species. Although the variations observed by de Vries in Œnothera had not, as has since been realized, the importance he gave to them, they led him to formulate conclusions very similar to those of the present mutation theory. According to de Vries the basic element of organic evolution is the *mutation*, a sudden variation, directly inherited, probably only affecting a single union of gametes (fertilized egg) of the original stock, strictly random from the point of view of adaptation, occurring with greater frequency in certain specific "periods of mutability", and giving rise to new elementary species, *selection* playing the same sorting rôle as in Darwinism but choosing among elementary species instead of working simply within one species. Thus it is a postulate common to mutation theory and to Darwinism that selection acts either on variations or on mutations; so one or the other would have to be such as could account for all the aspects of the evolutionary picture of the story of life.

Speaking very generally, we must grant that the mutation theory has an incontestable experimental foundation solidly based on the laboratory or the garden. Yet as a hypothesis explanatory of evolution it is open to very serious objections, some of which apply equally to Darwinism.

(*a*) Most mutations do not go outside the limits of species or genus, as is proved by morphology and also by the interfertility of mutants.

(*b*) In the vast majority of cases these mutations are recessive with respect to normal characteristics; that is, are dominated by them.

(*c*) They are almost always of a subtractive character, doubtless because they modify pre-existing genetic material but do not have the value of real innovations, truly additive.

(*d*) Many mutations have an undeniably pathological character, or even are incompatible with the organism's viability.

(e) They occur so rarely that in 1935 Haldane wrote that "until natural conditions are found exhibiting a considerably greater number of mutations than those so far known, mutations cannot be considered capable of alone causing large alterations of species".

(f) Even supposing that mutations such as generally occur give rise to selection in a sense which agrees with the facts, it seems they could never account for more than micro-evolution, and that they are powerless to explain not only the genesis of phyletic groups but the majority of adaptive and cooptative forms, as well as the generally progressive character of evolution considered as a whole.

SYNTHETIC THEORY

In his *Tempo and Mode in Evolution*[3] G. G. Simpson explains how there came, from an agreement between palaeontologists, geneticists and systematists, a convergence of opinions which allows a new synthesis of theories of evolution to be achieved. This new synthesis now being developed has been called neo-Darwinian because it assigns an important function to natural selection and refuses to allow the inheritance of acquired characteristics, vitalism, or teleology to play any part. It is nevertheless far removed from the neo-Darwinism of the Weismann school. It owes more to Darwin and his successors, but the great amount of knowledge accumulated since Darwin allows it to take quite new attitudes even to selection, and to incorporate many elements from other schools of evolutionary thought without following any of them particularly. The synthetic theory rests on the idea of the very subtle interplay of a series of "determinants of evolution", among which are inheritable variability, mutation rate, character of mutations, length of generations, size of population, and selection.

Population size, Simpson says (*op. cit.*, p. 66), plays an "essential rôle . . . as a determinant both of rates and of patterns

[3] Columbia Biological Series No. XV, Columbia University Press, 1944.

of evolution. Population size is in this connection more limited than in its vernacular sense. It refers to the genetically effective breeding population." In this case the problem becomes that of obtaining by the interplay of a sufficient number of factors (length of generations, size of populations, processes of segregation, etc.) a regular "drift" of the taxonomic types concerned. The synthetic theory thus finds itself, like Darwinism and the mutation theory, obliged to appeal to selection, and G. G. Simpson does not hesitate to write (*ibid.*, p. 80): "Only mutation supplies the materials of creation (whatever a mutation may be or however it may arise), but in the theories of population genetics it is selection that is truly creative,[4] building new organisms with these materials." From this point of view, despite the undoubted ingenuity of its mathematical apparatus and despite great skill in the choice of groups of factors able to confer on selection an increased effectiveness, there is no doubt the synthetic theory is laid open to most of the criticisms we have mentioned earlier.

We can also wonder whether it is really able to tackle, as its supporters claim it can, the problems of mega-evolution (quantum evolution), assuming straight away that this is not distinguished from phyletic evolution except by a difference of degree which yet permits a continuous insensible passage from one to the other. Quantum evolution, "the relatively rapid shift of a biotic population in disequilibrium to an equilibrium distinctly unlike an ancestral condition" (*ibid.*, p. 206), would constitute "the dominant and most essential process in the origin of taxonomic units of relatively high rank, such as families, orders, and classes" (*ibid.*), and would include "*circumstances that explain the mystery that hovers over the origins of such major groups*" (*ibid.*, my italics). It would imply "preadaptation as a necessary element" and would be due to transformations produced "at rapid but finite rates" rather than to sudden or instantaneous transformations (*ibid.*, p. 207). "Major examples of quantum evolution are never well-

[4] Doubtless these words must be understood only metaphorically, of the *results* of selection, not of selection as a "cause".

documented—indeed this deficiency of documentation is itself good evidence for the reality of the inferred phenomenon" (*ibid.*, p. 209). The genetic processes implied by quantum transformations would hardly allow of their happening at a single bound and "the selective processes do not make the unstable intermediate forms inviable" (*ibid.*, p. 210). In other words, "the accumulation of small mutations is not only adequate to permit rapid evolution, such as is involved in quantum evolution, but also theoretically the best substantiated mechanism for this" (*ibid.*, p. 211), this mechanism being supposed to work in the best way among "very small, isolated populations" (*ibid.*). While admitting the brilliance of this theory we cannot help thinking that it simply describes the mechanisms which *ought* to come into play (and this in the mesological* and mathematical conditions which would make them effective) to account for the relationships postulated by the evolutionary interpretation of the world of life, within the perspective of strictly orthodox Darwinism or mutation theory. The same also applies, in its different perspective, to the theory of paedomorphosis, which is our next concern.

PAEDOMORPHOSIS

We shall see later that some geneticists are rather worried about the part that mutations, as we know them, have been able to play in biological evolution. It is in fact difficult to see that these small mutations could be responsible for large variations such as lead to differentiation into orders, phyla and the other higher systematic groups. The theory of paedomorphosis refers those changes which produced the larger differences between the higher groups to the early stages of development of the germ, to ontogeny. Let us quote at length from G. R. de Beer's essay "Embryology and Taxonomy"[5]:

It is now clearly recognized that evolutionary novelties may make their appearance in any stage of the life-history, and may

[5] In *The New Systematics*, ed. Julian S. Huxley, Oxford University Press, 1940, pp. 376–8.

in subsequent generations become retarded, accelerated, or retain the same position in the time-scale of the ontogeny. In other words, it is just as possible that the adult descendant may resemble the ancestral adult. The former possibility appears to be much the more important, and since it accounts for the dropping-out from the life-history of the descendant of the adult characters of the ancestor, this condition may be known as "anti-recapitulation". It was pointed out by de Beer (*Embryology and Evolution*, Oxford, 1936) that the phylogenetic effects of largest systematic importance seem to be associated with evolutionary novelties which have either made their first appearance and exerted their main effects in early stages of ontogeny (cases of "caenogenesis" or "deviation"), or which have resulted in the retention of juvenile characters in the adult (cases of "neotony").

As an example of caenogenesis may be mentioned the embryonic membranes which distinguish the three highest classes of Chordata from the remainder as the Amniota. An example of deviation is provided by the sudden twist which gastropod larvae undergo and which, when it first occurred, was the starting point of what was to become the whole class. To neotony may be ascribed the origin of Chordata from organisms resembling echinoderm larvae, or of Insecta from the larvae of some myriapod-like forms. It is to be noted that in the last three cases there has been the production of a new type of adult organization, endowed with high potential for further evolution, and this process has been termed "paedomorphosis".

On the other hand, evolutionary novelties which exert their main effects at later stages of the life-histories (cases of adult variation and "acceleration") are less likely to produce large changes and may be supposed to give rise to mutants, subspecies, species and genera; such evolution is characterized by ever-increasing specialization and progressive loss of the potential for further evolution. This process is referred to as "gerontomorphosis". The study of ontogeny to find the stage of development at which the difference between types first becomes manifest, has been termed "phenogenetics" by Haecker ("Aufgaben und Ergebnisse der Phänogenetik", *Bibl. Genet.*, I (1925), 93): a field which appears to be of great promise.

It is concluded that, as evolution proceeds, paedomorphosis is succeeded by gerontomorphosis which actualizes the further evolutionary potentialities opened up by paedomorphosis and exhausts them. The group then lingers or becomes extinct unless a new bout of paedomorphosis supervenes. It is of interest to note that palaeontologists, among whom may be mentioned Wedekind and Beurlen, have on independent grounds come to the same conclusion regarding the occurrence of alternate bouts of "large" and "small" evolution. Schindewolf has also recognized the correlation between early ontogenetic appearance of the evolutionary novelty and systematic importance of the resulting new type. . . .

The importance of these matters in connection with the present discussion is that the *ultimate* systematic value of the new group is correlated with the time in ontogeny at which the variation made its effects manifest. Thus, when the larva of an ancestral untorted mollusc underwent its torsion (it would seem to have been sudden, for there are no intermediate stages of torsion; today it takes about two minutes in Acmoea), it provided a new type which was destined to become a class, out of which all Gastropoda have become differentiated. The idea that groups of potentially higher systematic value are formed rapidly during paedomorphic phases of evolution, and subsequently become split into groups of progressively restricted systematic value during gerontomorphic evolution, finds support in Matthew's study ("The Evolution of the Mammals in the Eocene", *Proc. zool. Soc. Lond.* 947, 1927) of the early history of the mammals. At the beginning of the tertiary period, many orders of mammals are already present, but they are represented by few types and are not yet diversified into the numerous families and genera which exist now. In other words, evolution had not proceeded very far in producing what Osborn called the "adaptive radiation" of the mammals.

A comparative study of embryos and adults of ancestors and descendants is thus able to support systematics in the view that there have been origins of phyla, classes, and orders, as well as origins of species, and to suggest a reason why some new types have lent themselves better than others to the formation of the groups of higher rank.

It seems to me that we have not yet sufficient certain facts om observation and experiment to support the hypothesis of such ontogenic mutations, but this hypothesis is an advance in that it concurs with the notion that "drosophilac" explanations[6] of evolution are not sufficient to account for the formation of the higher groups. Now we know that the most striking mark of good species is the possibility of crossing the individuals which it contains. We also know that this ability to interbreed rapidly disappears, often at the level of the genus, certainly at the level of the family. Supra-specific crosses are impossible in nature for various reasons, and so far as experiment is concerned, it would never enter any biologist's head to expect to succeed in fertilizing a sea-urchin's egg with mammalian sperm. I know that one could look for some evidence from experimental parthenogenesis or from teratology, but up to now, so far as I know, all the facts concern the species and below and none applies to levels above the species. It is moreover true that even if an experimenter can consciously impose on all parts of an embryo whatever conditions he choose, the normo-genetic development of the whole animal constitutes an optimum which it has not so far been possible to surpass.

There is a gap between the birth of life, which we imagine to have been unicellular, pluricellular or plasmodial,* and the earliest fossils. These last belong to different phyla, represented by some species which are now extinct and some which although so ancient have survived to our own day. The first branches are very ancient and palaeontology tells us they were diverse and numerous. So much is to be gathered from palaeontology. Crosses between individuals of different phyla seem impossible to us. In theory, changes in the germ, early in ontogeny, might perhaps explain the origin of the higher groups, but it would have to be claimed that the fertilized egg or zygote was affected very early by an unknown factor producing a very lucky mutation. Up to now experimental inter-

---

[6] One of the favourite laboratory animals for genetic experiments is the fruit-fly *Drosophila*, which has many advantages, the chief being that it has only four large chromosomes. There is a tendency among some geneticists to generalize from experience with *Drosophila*, much as some experimental psychologists generalize about animal, or even human, behaviour from experience with rats.

ference with the germ-cells has produced monsters or various modifications, such as change of sex, for example, but it has never had any effect beyond the limits of the one type being used. Such ontogenetic changes may have existed in the early stages of life's story, but it looks as though the larger phenomena of evolution—the formation of higher groups, phyla, etc.—have now stopped appearing.

THE PSYCHIC FACTOR OF EVOLUTION

Some writers attribute a place among the factors of biological evolution to what we may call *psyche*. It is an ancient idea and has often been used to define life itself. By it is meant principally the unconscious *psyche* which begins with the *irritability* (capacity to respond to a stimulus) of the most elementary living things, which is manifested in the invention at various levels observed in animals, and explicit in the reflective thought of man. This psychic factor is at the basis of the Gestalt psychology, according to which the concept of form (*Gestalt*) is a synthetic and organizing concept which is as much opposed to the associationists' analysis as to neo-Darwinian selection by happy good fortune. For Gestalt psychologists *psyche* is above all *organization*. Perception is the organization of locomotive mechanisms; memory is the preservation of an organized structure; the intellect is organization adapted to an end. Thus *psyche* corresponds with the transfer to the levels of perception and action of that power of organization of the living creature which shows itself at a lower level in the phenomena of assimilation, ontogenesis, regeneration, etc. So *psyche* appears to us as the form taken by evolution when it reaches the higher levels of animal life. Intelligence is the present culmination of the organization of the living creature, just as man is today at the highest point on the ladder of evolution.

Since some writers claim that there is a duality of matter and form in the composition of any given living thing, or suppose that the stuff of the universe has two complementary attributes, material and spiritual, then *psyche*, conceived philosophically in very different ways, will be at times invoked as one factor along with others in the evolution of living things, and not regarded simply as an epiphenomenon emerging in the course of and as a result of that evolution.

CHAPTER VII

THE TERMINOLOGY OF
EVOLUTION

Evolutionary biologists often use terms which, when properly considered, seem to correspond to a mixture of empirical science and metaphysics. Nothing could now be more fitting than to try to make clear the meanings of these ambiguous expressions, which can only "resolve" problems by providing purely verbal solutions if they are accepted without careful distinctions being made. We shall examine some of these terms in this chapter.

ORTHOGENESIS

The word seems to have been used first by Haacke (1893) and to have achieved a wider circulation since Eimer (1897). Etymologically it means development in a straight line, and it is often associated with the idea of preadaptation. Organisms, it has been suggested, contain within themselves as predetermined their lines of development, so that they follow these of necessity and cannot follow others; but they do not follow them spontaneously, and if they pass from one form to another they do so strictly under the influence of external factors. But a good many biologists have made use of the term, and attributed to it various meanings. Some consider the idea of orthogenesis as corresponding to a fact of biological observation, but strip it of all metaphysical implications. Others see in it a fact surrounded by a philosophical aura from which it seems to them difficult to escape. Others again insist on the progressive character of orthogenesis without drawing from that any theoretical conclusions. Lastly, there are palaeontologists who dispute the reality of orthogenesis, or at least tend severely to limit its meaning. We cannot now embark on an exhaustive study of this question, for this would need considerable development and expansion. We shall content ourselves with presenting with the help of some significant quotations a few examples of different viewpoints.

Let us look first at Grassé's *Précis de biologie animale*[1]:

Orthogenesis or straight-line evolution is well-known, thanks to the great discoveries of modern palaeontology. Every evolutionary line is traced back by the naturalist who takes into account the orthogenetic direction which is his guiding thread among the chaos of fossil forms. Many authors consider orthogenetic only those phyla in which certain organs show an excessive development or hypertrophy. In fact, such orthogenesis is only a particular case of the rule according to which evolution unfolds itself in a predetermined direction. We shall see that sometimes orthogenesis is hidden by evolutionary radiations. We distinguish two sorts of orthogenesis:

A. *Hypertelic orthogenesis:* in which an organ acquires by successive stages an excessive development; e.g., the upper canines of carnivores of the group *Machairodus* (the sabretooths) and the horns of the titanotheres.

B. *Coordinated orthogenesis:* which concerns a group of organs or even a whole organism and is carried through with a close coordination of the variations in the different parts and ends in a stable structure. (Our author gives us as an example of coordinated orthogenesis the evolution of the horse.)

For us, the term orthogenesis is synonymous with straight-line evolution, *but we remove from it any mysterious quality of predetermination* [my italics]. The evolution of a particular line of descent takes place in a certain way, and that is all there is to it. It is simply a matter of the statement or, at most, of the objective description of the facts. Straight-line evolution is a fact to be explained just like any other.

[1] 5th edition, Paris, Masson et Cie, 1957, p. 1319.

As for Professor Cuénot, he often returned to the theme of orthogenesis in his last work.[2] As many writers do, he distinguishes progressive processes (*hypermorphoses* and *hypertelies*) from *eumorphoses* or *eutelies*, which correspond to the coordinated orthogenesis of Grassé. But he does not, like Grassé, cheerfully abandon the idea of preadaptation, and writes:

Orthogenesis can be thought of as a series of preadaptations. In fact, to put the matter simply, orthogenesis appears as a sequence of species each of which is preparatory to the following, down to that which seems to be the end of the process. Thus the walking foot of the tetrapods surely preceded actual movement on a hard, resistant earth; the feather must have come before the wing—how could birds fly without feathers? Dental structure which requires a particular mode of feeding, without however making such a mode absolutely necessary, must surely be a preadaptation? More, such dentition must be in harmony with the rest of the organism, the method and speed of movement, the chemistry of the stomach and of the intestine, and the sense-organs. It must all go together. As Cuvier said, we cannot imagine a state of things where there would be flies and no swallows, or vice versa. The complex structures of a nervous system always appear to be anterior to the moment when they are used, or the moment when they become indispensable for organized behaviour. The brain, with its complicated structure, begins with the lower primates; it undeniably existed before that of *Homo sapiens*. In the same realm of ideas it has been noted that nest-dwelling birds with a more complicated behaviour have a more complicated brain than nidifugous birds.

Cuénot never completely gave up the idea of preformation, for in the chapter in which he deals with the uncertainties of biological evolution he still writes (p. 536):

Palaeontologists, however, conceive all orthogenesis as the development of a *tendency* or evolutionary potency, predetermined in the common (reconstructed) ancestral form. They freely compare it with the unfolding of pre-formed ontogenesis

[2] *L'Évolution biologique*, Paris, Masson, 1951.

in the egg. With the passing of time the tendency realizes itself more and more, unless there is a chance interruption of the orthogenetic process by external causes. "Tendency" is clearly only a form of expression, indicating a state of mind of the observer, but not referring to or to be resolved into any mechanism of the material world. The word is attached to many metaphysical concepts, notably that of the developmental force of the botanist Göbel (*immanente Entfalkungstrieb*). . . . Although I rank explanation by orthogenesis among the uncertainties, yet personally I incline to the palaeontological view, despite the metaphysical smell—or mustiness. I think that those forms which are at the beginnings of lines of descent, great or insignificant, have potentially in themselves the future of their species, but the effects of the environment, that is, chance, interfere with this possible development. Just as ontogenesis is the preparation of the future of the individual, so orthogenesis is the preparation of the future of lines of descent.

Let us now hand over the argument to a palaeontologist who died recently, Teilhard de Chardin.[3] For this author, biological evolution obeys a law of directional complication, which has been given the name of orthogenesis. "Claiming that this term, orthogenesis, has been used in different senses, debatable or restricted, or else that it has a metaphysical flavour, certain biologists would simply suppress it. My considered opinion is on the contrary that the word is essential and irreplaceable, in order to mark and affirm the property clearly possessed by living matter of forming a system," within which the terms demonstrably *follow one another* with constantly increasing degrees of centro-complexity. "Thanks to the power of incremental change which characterizes it, living substance is 'weighted' with complexity and instability. It falls, or more exactly it rises, into more and more unlikely forms. Without orthogenesis there would be only a chaotic spreading-out: with orthogenesis life incontestably moves upwards." In the same line of thinking, with regard to the formation of the noösphere, Fr Teilhard explains by the effects of orthogenesis the progressive development of the brain which in fact culminates in

[3] *Le Phénomène humain*, éd. du Seuil, 1955, p. 114.

man. "By 'orthogenesis', in the etymological and most general
sense of the term, must be understood here, I repeat, the
fundamental 'drift' according to which the stuff of the universe
behaves in our eyes as moving towards corpuscular conjunc-
tions ever more complex in their material arrangements and
psychologically ever more inwardly organized—a 'drift', let us
say, directly written into higher living things as a growing
concentration of the nervous system." The reader will perhaps
have noticed that Fr Teilhard, freely taking a phenomenological
viewpoint, makes no reference to the idea of predetermination.
It seems probable that for him the law of directional complication which has been given the name of orthogenesis is
more or less equivalent to Grassé's straight-line evolution
which, according to the quotation we have given from his work,
does not imply any predetermination.

We shall moreover see, since we are trying to draw up a
kind of theoretical and scientific balance-sheet for the concept
of orthogenesis, that this idea itself, with or without irrational
implications, is not the object of general agreement among
biologists. G. G. Simpson and those evolutionists who can be
taken as standing more or less close to his position are among
those who criticize the concept itself. G. G. Simpson, a supporter of the synthetic theory of evolution, does not however,
while criticizing it, do away with the notion of orthogenesis
altogether. Among the "theorems on inertia in evolution"[4]
occur these two:

"A tendency for phyla to continue to evolve in much the
same direction for considerable periods of time, rectilinear
evolution or orthogenesis in a purely descriptive sense, is a
common evolutionary phenomenon."

"Observed rectilinear sequences are usually most consistent
with the theory that orthoselection is a dominant or primary
factor, and some are not logically explicable in any other way."

The complex and integrated interaction of internal and external factors is the essence of the synthetic theory, and those
evolutionists who can be grouped with Simpson look mostly to

[4] *Tempo and Mode in Evolution*, pp. 177–8.

the environment for their causes (the directional influence of Darwin's natural selection), but an environment which works also by producing genetic combinations and systems which would not have been brought into being by the influence of internal processes only.

THE IDEA OF TRIAL AND ERROR

In the writings of many biologists the notion of trial and error is often used to express the idea of a fumbling advance in the process of evolution. Sometimes the same authors declare themselves to be at the same time supporters of the theory of orthogenesis, which implies a contradiction at least in so far as they cannot consider this latter process as a line, broken in parts but having an end somewhere all the same. In Fr Teilhard's speculations, for example, the idea is frequently found in various forms of expression that the essential superiority of human activity is a development by trial and error of a potentiality immanent in living matter. So it is for him with "research": "In a very general way we can say, indeed we must say, that research, this being defined as an effort to go on endlessly discovering by the method of trial and error better biological arrangements, represents one of the fundamental properties of living matter. Taken now strictly in its usual sense of intelligently directed trial and error, research is then necessarily as old as the awakening of thought on earth."

THE IDEA OF TENDENCY

In an interesting lecture on the subject, "The first experiments and successes of life", J. Piveteau[5] also speaks of *tendencies*, which implies at bottom the adoption of the fundamental idea of orthogenesis.

Life contains in itself at its beginning various tendencies which, in becoming realized, become opposed to one another. There are tendencies which end by becoming incompatible and then there is division. To understand all the characteristics of

[5] *Quatorzième semaine de synthèse*, Paris, Albin Michel, 1952.

life we must also take into account the distinction between animal and vegetable. Only these two together give a complete picture of life. There are two fundamental tendencies: the vegetal, which infuses life into matter; and the animal, which goes further and higher, towards mind. I cannot explain this fact, and I do not think that positive science can explain it.

As we have already remarked, Cuénot likewise supposes that orthogenesis, if it is not emptied of all intuitive content, presents itself as the "development of a tendency".

These few examples, which it would be easy to multiply and to enlarge upon, appear to show that everything happens as if, struck by the regular character of the story of living things, insufficiently convinced of the "omnipotence" of natural selection, and impressed by the great originality of living matter and its ability to master its environment (so manifest in the course of ontogeneses), many evolutionists felt the need of a "variability" in living matter which should not be quite unpredictable or irregular, but endowed with some characteristics (tendency to diversity, power of discovery, predetermination, opportunism, etc.), capable of facilitating the unfolding of the processes of orthogenesis, of adaptations involving both form and function together, and of that progressive occupation of all biotopes* that are eventually "free", by all of which the development of life is made manifest. Such expressions, allowable on the level of the *description* of phenomena, take on a metaphysical significance when they are presented as *explanations*, or else they remain purely verbal forms of expression. The examination of these expressions would be worth a discussion such as we cannot open here, but at any rate it has been important to notice the problem in passing.

CHAPTER VIII

SCIENTIFIC DIFFICULTIES OF THE GENERAL THEORY OF EVOLUTION

In his *Phénomène humain* Teilhard de Chardin, after admitting the "tree of life drawn by Professor Cuénot", writes that "we can draw from the simple contemplation of extrinsic forms strength and a lesson: the obviousness of his evidence. There are yet in the world a few minds still suspicious or sceptical in the matter of evolution. Knowing nature, and naturalists, only in books they think that the evolutionists' battle is always fought as in Darwin's time. And because argument continues about the mechanism by which species could have originated, they imagine that biology is hesitant—or even that it could be hesitant without suicide—about the fact and reality of such evolution." Later too, after more discussion, he says:

> After that, we can go on for years yet arguing about the manner in which this organic world, this enormous organism, can have arisen; the more we learn of its frightful complexity the more dizzy we feel. How can we reconcile this continuous growth with the determinism of molecules, the blind interplay of chromosomes, the apparent inability of individuals' favourable adaptations to be transmitted by heredity? How in other words can we reconcile the external, "teleological", evolution of phenotypes with the internal, mechanistic, evolution of genotypes? We can no longer manage to understand, by taking it to pieces, how this machine moves forward. Maybe; but while we

wait the machine is before us—and it *goes*. Because chemistry cannot yet tell us how granites are formed, can we deny that the continents go on making more granite? Like *everything* in a universe where time is finally set up and integrated (I shall return to this) as a fourth dimension, life is and can only be an evolutionary dimension of nature. Physically and historically it corresponds to a certain function X which defines in space, duration, and form, the "position" of each living thing. This is the fundamental fact which requires explanation, certainly, but for which the evidence is now beyond all verification, as it is also protected from all further experimental or observational contradiction.[1]

The last sentence is particularly rash. It is true that science records the facts of evolution. But it is one thing to record them and seek to explain them, and another thing to claim that evolution is the universal master key of life. So we are bound, before we apply ourselves to the evidence, which looks as though it is not entirely free from subjective elements, to examine some difficulties which the theory of inheritance seems to us to raise. We realize that these difficulties are relevant to a generalized theory of evolution rather than to the principle of evolution, but they are serious enough to cast doubt upon the value of that principle itself, so far as it is applied to present and past living things.[2]

HEREDITY

On the hypothesis, which for many people is a proven fact, of descendance of living things from a common stock, the essential factor in the growth and diversification of the genealogical tree is heredity. Now if we try to derive from what we know about heredity some support for this genealogical hypothesis, we come up against some rather disturbing facts.

[1] *Op. cit.*, p. 151.
[2] Some of these difficulties have already been noted in Chapter VI when we were setting out a summary of the principal explanatory theories of evolution.

Interfertility

The species we know today do not cross naturally among themselves: they are intersterile. Can we imagine a time when, in some past geological era, it was different and fertile crosses were possible from pairs of parents belonging to different genera or families? From the fact that very ancient species like the nautilus or the lingulids have survived to and still exist in our own day we can conclude that the general conditions of life (temperature, solar radiation, chemical composition of the atmosphere, the oceans, the continents and the food supplies, etc.) have not sensibly changed since the first origins of living things, in spite of geological changes and periods of long duration like the glaciations. One can therefore claim that since the basic physical conditions of life have been maintained for millions of years it is difficult to think that the conditions of reproduction—a phenomenon closely linked with nutrition— have changed, while the nutritional conditions have remained the same. If this argument is valid, we may doubt whether the species which have inhabited and now inhabit our world do derive from common roots by descendance, or another explanation of their origin ought to be looked for.

Genetics

The first evolutionists, Lamarck and Darwin, attributed the origin of individual variation in living things to the action of external factors, environmental or mesological,* as we have recalled earlier. Lamarck explained the persistence and the growth of initial variations by the inheritance of acquired characteristics; Darwin invoked natural selection as the principal factor in the evolution of species. Neither of these two writers knew the concept of *individual character* (e.g., the colour of the eyes or skin) which is now familiar to us. This idea, and the laws governing the hereditary transmission of these characters, are owed to Mendel. These laws and their working suggest the existence of very small, very stable units as material substrates of the individual characters, which were later called *genes*. The origin of genetic variation was attributed, by de Vries, to chance. Variation becomes evident in individuals by a well-marked deviation from the original type, as happens for Mendelian characters. De Vries gave it the name *mutation*. It has kept that name in biology, not only as the unit of individual variability but also, influenced by Lamarckian and Darwinian ideas, as the unit of trans-specific variability, and as the unit of evolution *tout court*.

With all this in mind we may try to see whether the data of genetics throw any light on the problem of descendance. Here again the outlook of this young science is not very encouraging. The spontaneous or experimentally-produced mutations we observe nowadays are not on the same scale as the great changes which the formation of the higher systematic groups presupposes. Cuénot and Rostand wrote in 1936[3]:

> We have indeed seen mutation, we see it continually pro-ducing novelties of detail, and modifying what already exists, but we do not see it creating in an individual of any species organs unknown in that species, or showing the great con-structive powers that it must have had if it was alone responsible for all the variety of life.... But even with these reservations, we must say again quite firmly that apart from mutations there are only shadows, and wherever in one's explanation of evolu-tion one rejects the mechanism of mutations one is forced to have recourse to "unknown factors".

At an international colloquium in 1947 Cuénot had evidently hardly changed his opinions[4]:

> We must not ask of genetics, an essentially experimental science, more than it can give. It gives a very satisfactory account of micro-evolution, which is something, since evolution is a succession of species; but it remains almost dumb when it comes to the origins of the higher groups, to orthogeneses which look as though they follow a line already mapped out in advance, to the astonishing variety of organic life, to the ever-perfect complementarity of fauna and flora. Genetics is clearly only concerned with chance phenomena: mutations are de-

[3] L. Cuénot et J. Rostand: *Introduction à la génétique*, Paris, Centre de documentation universitaire, 1936.

[4] In *Paléontologie et transformisme*, Paris, A. Michel, p. 251.

termined by the chance concatenation of the inherited genetic make-up and external agents (radiation, perhaps). Their success, that is, the birth of new species, is the effect of chance, pre-adapted organisms meeting by good luck the environment which suits them. Besides, many biologists have the feeling, difficult to express in words, that are like worn pennies which have been in circulation a long time, that alongside of chance must be set something else, which gives a profound meaning to life, to continual evolution, to the birth of mind; in short, a sense of purpose. This is only a feeling, but for my part I prefer it to the narrow positivism of materialist philosophy.

J. Rostand, reconsidering in 1953 the relations between genetics and evolution, resigned himself to thinking that the "evolutionary potential" is less now than it was in the past. The world of life is stable, fixed, and no longer shows any evidence of those activities which must have brought it into existence. It is certainly a fact that for hundreds of millions of years life has shown none but minor innovations, of detail only, never having brought into being any new type of structure, any new *cladus*.

MICRO- AND MACRO-EVOLUTION[5]

We saw just now that Cuénot, a whole-hearted evolutionist, admitted that genetics gave a good account of micro-evolution, but was more or less dumb so far as concerned the origins of the higher groups. This opinion is very like that of Vialleton, whom we quoted in Chapter III as distinguishing organizational types from formal types. Contrary to what one might believe from reading recent writers, who avoid quoting Vialleton (probably because he spoke of the "evolutionary illusion"), while they admit the differences between the lower systematic groups, contemporary palaeontologists and neontologists often come up against the problem raised by the morphological gap

[5] This distinction, foreshadowed by Vialleton, was worked out by R. Goldschmidt (*The Material Basis of Evolution*, New Haven, Yale University Press, 1940), whose macro-evolution corresponds to the mega-evolution of G. G. Simpson.

separating off the "organizational types". Simply to say that these types belong to the story of macro- or mega-evolution clearly does not solve the problem. It becomes that of the mechanisms capable of explaining in practice these (supposed) modes of evolution *by descent*. Now *at present* nothing allows us to explain satisfactorily the origin of the higher groups: neither small *mutations* of the classical type, nor the various *genetic mechanisms* postulated to supply what is needed as a cause but for which no experimental proof has been possible (the simultaneous occurrence of numerous micro-mutations; isolated large gene-mutations; chromosomal aberrations; systematic recombinations of numerous dominant characters; radical recombination of pre-existent genetic characters by the segregation of homozygote animals; allopolyploidy*; or even indeed the propagation in a species of a new kind of proteins, analogous to the viruses which cause illnesses, but producing alterations which could not be considered pathological), nor *onto-mutations*, nor certain processes like *neoteny* or the *paedomorphosis* the possible effects of which G. R. de Beer envisaged some thirty years ago.[6] To say, as is often done, that it would betray a narrowness of mind to reduce a process as impressive as organic evolution to one or two simple mechanisms, ought not to imply that that process is to be explained by recourse to many mechanisms together, all more or less hypothetical (small mutations, Dobzhansky's cataclysmic mutations, segregation, neoteny, onto-mutations, allopolyploidy, interspecific hybrids, selection, etc.). This leads us naturally to confront the data of palaeontology with those of neontology: the clashes between them explain the difficulty of reconciling the "fact" of evolution and its "mechanisms", whatever they are decided to be.

PALAEONTOLOGY AND NEONTOLOGY

To put it as briefly as possible, we can say that the evidence of palaeontology suggests *transformations*, and the (plausible)

[6] G. R. de Beer, *Embryology and Evolution*, Oxford, 1930.

hypothesis of descent allows us to account for these; but our neontological knowledge suggests a comparative *stability* of living forms, and offers no clear examples of variability except within the species or, exceptionally, the genus. This contradiction could, it is true, be removed by the idea of a purposive evolution, but this sort of metaphysical explanation is ruled out (methodologically) by most scientists, depending on how much they want to stay on the purely scientific level. In this case, three principal issues may be considered, which might remove the contradiction.

The time factor

One of the most important gaps in evolutionary theory results from our uncertainties about the effects of the time factor. To the arguments of geneticists who can only observe small mutations, it is replied that the large mutations which gave rise to organizational types (macro- or mega-evolution) are the result of a long preparatory period. Palaeontology ranges over millions of years: it is practically incommensurable with neontology, which only deals with the experience of tens of years. Even in the best-equipped modern laboratory we cannot dispose of the immensities of geological time, and so we cannot safely deny the action of the time factor in producing the higher organizational types. Today, we can merely say that such action is *possible*, while remembering that the living things which originated long ago have not sensibly changed since the geological era in which they are found for the first time. This is not an irrefutable objection, however, and it seems we must recognize that the real rôle of time, on the geological scale, must in practice remain unknown to us.

Present causes

Two attitudes are possible towards the data of neontological experiment and observation: the one attributes to these data an unconditional "applicability" which the other denies to them. According to supporters of the first view to look upon present micro-evolution and past macro-evolution as two separate processes determined by essentially different factors would be practically to admit, like the early geo-morphologists, that the great geological phenomena were brought about by at present unknown, cataclysmic, forces. If Lyell's great merit—and it was indeed very great—was to have assumed the action of "present causes" in long-past phenomena, it would seem fair to recognize the same merit in modern theories of evolution which seek to do away with all differences between past and present phenomena. Those who think in this way would say that what applies to present species *ought* to apply to the continuously evolving phyla of palaeontology. In opposition to this attitude Teilhard de Chardin says[7]:

> A good many changes on this earth that we should have sworn had stopped a long time ago are still going on in the world around us. As a consequence of this unexpected statement, which gratifies our natural preference for dealing with perceptible and tractable, sensible forms, our minds gently slip into thinking that there has never been in the past, any more than there could be in the future, anything absolutely new under the sun. Slip a bit further, and we restrict real knowledge to *present* events only. At bottom, is not everything simply "conjecture" apart from the present? We must at all costs react against this instinctive limitation of the rights and domain of science.

We shall try to show later that despite the geological and other changes in the earth since living things first appeared, life goes on today in the same way as in the past, and consequently its *general* conditions have always been the same. This conclusion favours the use of present causes in interpreting the past. All the same the problem arises again if one says, as some writers do, that the present representatives of the various phyla which have persisted to our age carry the signs of a certain ageing, of a gerontomorphosis stabilizing them in a state incompatible with variability of any magnitude. Such ageing cannot however be attributed to phyla except in a metaphorical way, and their extinction was due to some other cause than

[7] *Le Phénomène humain*, p. 101.

senility. It is certainly possible to believe that the *germ plasm* is able in the course of time to undergo either a steady evolution (conformable or not to the law of entropy) or a series of dichotomies of the type postulated for example by the theory of hologenesis,[8] as a result of which the specific variability would progressively be reduced. Such a process, the effects of which would be much the same as those of ageing, remains extremely hypothetical but its possibility cannot at present be denied altogether.

Unknown causes

In the end, in face of the various difficulties we have just mentioned, two extreme attitudes are possible. The first maintains the validity of the most general notion of evolution, as a necessary methodological supposition, and its unconditional applicability to everything science can deal with. On this view, the failure of the various hypotheses suggested to account for the evolutionary picture of the world of life ought logically to lead to the third of the expedients previously referred to and which J. Rostand formulated a few years ago in this way: "All things considered, we do not ourselves think there is any need to be completely stumped by the apparent 'trilemma'—chance, design, Lamarckism; among these three explanations, one incomplete, the second illusory, the third disproved by experience, what is the advantage in choosing? In dealing with the problem of evolution, as in so many other cases, the wisest and fairest attitude would be to leave room for the unknown: but one should be careful neither to name this unknown nor to make it unknowable."

The second attitude considers that the difficulties are the direct consequences of the evolutionary interpretation and are sufficiently serious to throw doubt on the interpretation itself. We cannot here follow up the idea that these two attitudes might be equally fruitful on the level of neontological research though apparently not equally conformable to the dreams of

[8] D. Rosa, *L'Ologénèse; nouvelle théorie de l'évolution et de la distribution géographique des êtres vivants* (Felix Alcan, Paris, 1931).

modern man, drunk as he is with the power and freedom of science. We cannot say that it is at present possible to choose with certainty between these two opinions; we can say that our own opinion is that from a sufficiently lofty philosophical standpoint this choice is, taking it all round, pretty unimportant.

CHANGE AND PERMANENCE IN THE LIVING WORLD

We have said before that for many contemporary scientists evolution is the sole theme of the cosmic trilogy, the "Open, Sesame!" to the whole of nature. We should like to show here, while limiting ourselves to the field of biology, that certain facts lead us to modify the notions of becoming and change by that of permanence or stability. There is no question of denying change. Change is an empirical idea, experimentally verified, and imposed by experience on all observers. But to speak of change is to make implicit reference to something which changes and which, before it changes, presents a collection of definite characters which is often called a *state*; so we say that ice is in a solid state before it passes to the liquid state under the action of heat.

Now notice that in this very simple example the successive states are not irreversible and do not involve a substantial change—a change in the chemical structure. Molecules of water, H_2O, are always there in ice, water or water vapour: the action of heat (within the normal limits) increases or lessens the density of molecules of H_2O in a given volume, but does not alter its chemical composition. We can thus say that a permanence of chemical composition persists or subsists under the different physical states of matter. These very elementary considerations at any rate show that room must be made in the interpretation of natural phenomena for permanence alongside of change, and an attempt made to analyse their relationships. This is what physics also teaches us. For physics shows that none of the objects we judge to be permanent really is so. When we see a thing, it is because it produces a light-phenomenon—that is, like all phenomena, a *change*. Since science can only deal with changes, how can science admit the idea of a permanent object? There seems to be a contradiction implicit in thinking that beneath every change is something which continues to exist despite the change. But the contradiction disappears if we think of an object as formed of elements which are themselves unchanging but whose different arrangements and relationships give rise to phenomena. Such, for example, are the fundamental particles of modern physics, which can nevertheless only be known by and through the phenomena they produce, so that it is true to say that they are defined by their relations with the rest of the universe.

Let us get back to the idea of a *state*. The word always implies a sort of halt called for a time in the onward march of phenomena, or at least a more typical, characteristic phase in a series of related phenomena. These "halts" can be as short as any other phase in the series considered, but they are more "striking". Our minds need points of reference: without them there would be no reflection and knowledge would be impossible. Moreover, some states persist, sometimes indefinitely, and become what is called in everyday language stable or permanent. It is difficult not to grant that certain igneous rocks dating from the formation of the earth's crust must have remained unchanged from that time to the present. It is true that the mineral world undergoes metamorphosis in some parts, but some parts remain unchanging. We shall therefore say that in practice change and permanence exist together and that a total account of the world must include both and try to reconcile them.

It is common knowledge that living things are not independent of the physical environment because they draw their nourishment from it; but that they also preserve in this *external* environment a certain autonomy. This is achieved by *internal* factors fundamentally proper to living creatures, which when joined with the external factors ensure the permanence of life on earth. To illustrate these general remarks we shall give a few examples of permanence which the world of life shows us.

Permanence of the biotope of the earth

A biotope is a geographical place where a certain living population develops best, and it is immediately obvious that the size, the extension, of biotopes varies a good deal. For example, man can live anywhere on earth, because his intelligence enables him to preserve his physiological equilibrium artificially. Plants and animals are necessarily more restricted. The biotope of the earth, as we have called it, is the collection of external factors needed for life's continuance: for example, water, fresh or salt; an atmosphere; food; the sun's radiation; and perhaps cosmic radiation. True, the elements also cause crises: earthquakes, volcanic eruptions, floods, tidal races, typhoons, storms, etc. But the effects of such catastrophes are limited in so far as the mean level of the external factors of life has remained to all intents and purposes constant since the beginning of life, and so they play their part in ensuring life's permanence.

Ubiquity of certain living forms in that biotope

We have just remarked that thanks to various artificial aids man can inhabit any part of the earth. This privilege is not peculiar to man. Some very small, and probably very ancient, living things, constituting an anaerobic, heterotrophic, telluric flora, have been studied by A. R. Prévot of the Institut Pasteur[9]: "A number of samples have been taken of earth, river mud, and sea and lake bottoms, in France, Europe, America, Africa, Greenland, on the equator, in the tropics, and lately, thanks to Paul-Émile Victor's party in Adelie Land, at the South Pole. . . . This microflora is essentially made up of a group always found in all places where such samples have been taken, composed of the following species: *Clostridium bifermantans*, *Cl. valerienum*; *Cl. caproicum* more or less mixed with *Cl. sporogenes* and *Welchia perfringens*; and a group often but not always found in which the species are just as different among themselves, but where the dominant genus

[9] "L'Ubiquité des bactéries anaérobies et la notion nouvelle de 'microflore originelle' ", *La Nature*, No. 3229, May, 1952.

is Cillobacterium." This is an original microflora which Prévot defines as "the microflora of virgin soil before man intervenes. We only know now the original heterotrophic, anaerobic flora. It remains to find the autotrophic, chimiotrophic and allotrophic parts, both of the anaerobic and of the aerobic kinds." Granted the immense importance of bacteria in nature, and their part in all vital reactions, the conclusion that the biologist is daily forced to accept is that life is a symbiosis of bacteria and their hosts.

Permanence of the natural equilibrium

The question of the ubiquity of certain bacteria leads us naturally to remark on the general part played by these microorganisms in the world as a whole. Let us quote a general textbook of zoology[10]:

> But in this community [a pond], as in a big town, the animals are constantly producing waste matter, and death results in the constant addition of animal bodies to the water. These waste matters would eventually choke up the pond and bring all life to an end were it not for a further step. We often look upon the bacteria solely as enemies of man, as agents of disease. There are, however, many extremely useful bacteria, and certain of these are responsible for the breaking-down and the change of deleterious waste nitrogenous substances (the excreta of animals) and the carcases of animals into simple substances like nitrates. The result of the action of these bacteria is the preparation of certain very important food stuffs for the green organisms, which again build up the more complex organic substances so necessary as animal food. With this there is a complete cycle in the pond. . . . The higher green plants make use of nitrates and ammonia as their sources of nitrogen, and they transform these substances into amino-acids, amides, and eventually to proteins. These are devoured by animals, and in modified form take part in the construction of their bodies. When waste nitrogenous substances are excreted or the animal dies, these nitrogenous compounds are broken up by various kinds of bacteria until ultimately simple stable substances are again reached, like

[10] W. S. Dakin, *Elements of General Zoology*, Oxford University Press, 1928, pp. 411–12.

nitrates and nitrites, ammonia and even free nitrogen. Other bacteria may build up ammonia and nitrogen into proteins again, or into nitrites and nitrates; the green plant utilizes the latter, and so the cycle goes on.

Permanence of general properties of living things: the two conceptions of "biosphere"

The word was introduced by the geologist Suess to mean purely and simply the physical division of the world made up of the collection of all living things, past and present. So taken, in its primitive sense, the expression is useful and does not raise any difficulties. Teilhard de Chardin, however, gave it a new meaning: he used it to mean Life (with a capital) which is not, it is true, a universal organism of which living things are the elements or parts, but is for him a physical reality of a separate order characterized by perfectly determinate, specific properties. This conception is exposed to various criticisms which we shall not examine here; it is nevertheless usable from the point of view under consideration in this chapter. But first we must be more exact about physical reality. It is difficult to see how living things taken collectively could constitute a physical reality. Life is common to all living things, but like other universals its unity is abstract, conceptual. It is more than simply a label, more than an empty, meaningless word; it is the objective content of a universal idea. Every life is a strictly individual perfection. A collection of individuals cannot, in consequence of the proper life of each, have more than a metaphorical life: such, for example, is the life of the family or of the nation. The life of the biosphere is therefore not a physical reality. It is only a physical reality in concrete living things. In the mind, it has a rational "existence" which does not correspond to any independent physical reality.

Nevertheless the idea of life is founded in reality, in individual living things. There subsist under their diversity, from the most simple to the most complex, fundamental properties which are common to all and which, united by the mind, allow some footing to the idea of living substance. But it must never be lost sight of that living substance is never independent of living things themselves, and is found in all beneath the varieties of composition that they present, all living things having the same general fundamental properties, from the lowliest to the highest. Thus the stability of the biosphere, considered as a physical unity, is the stability of the fundamental characters of life in living things which differ from one another morphologically and functionally. So we get back to present views supporting the idea of the permanence of certain properties of the biosphere.

Permanence of characters common to all living things

Let us see what a biochemist has to say about this permanence[11]:

> The temptation to emphasize the diversity of living phenomena must be resisted at the very outset; the similarity of all living tissues is the fundamental observation to be made. The proteins from sources as diverse as human finger-nail and the contents of a bacterial cell are constructed from the same amino-acids. In spite of the enormous number of sugars which the organic chemist declares, and indeed demonstrates by synthesis, to be possible, the living world gets along with a handful. The same vitamin is essential for the growth of certain bacteria, of a certain beetle, of a certain mammal, although outwardly these three organisms present very few resemblances except the general property of being alive.
>
> It may well be that these repetitions of chemical structure, which might appear to be the result of arbitrary selection, are the result of restrictions inherent in living matter, restrictions which are less obvious to the observer than those imposed by the nature of the atmosphere and the gases which occur in it, the waters of the earth and the dissolved substances which they contain, and the limits of temperature fixed by the conditions of the planet. All must tend to create uniformity.

The same author ends this chapter—"The Biochemist Explores Life"—with these words: "The exploration we have

[11] J. S. D. Bacon, *The Chemistry of Life*, London, Watts, 2nd edn, 1947, pp. 58–9.

made of the charted regions of biochemistry has brought once more the conclusion that life is more notable for its similarities than for its diversities, claiming the right to be regarded as a single phenomenon wherever it may be encountered." These paragraphs confirm the permanence of the fundamental characters of life, giving them a permanent chemical basis throughout biological time.

Permanence of certain living forms

It has long been noted as a singular and enigmatic fact that very simple forms persist alongside of the higher ones; at the present day there exist side by side forms which can be thought of as various stages of evolution. There are a number of positive facts to support this generalization.

(i) *Protista*: Thoroughgoing evolutionists are generally agreed that the protozoa and protophyta were the first living things: unicellular animals and plants, and what is more, fairly complicated. It is interesting to contemplate in passing the prodigious multiplicative capacity of the world of protista. If the reproduction of a single bacterium went on unobstructed, in less than three days the bulk of its complete progeny would equal that of the whole earth. The very absurdity of such a possibility is sufficient to demonstrate that in nature some factors must intervene—some extremely effective factors—to restrict the multiplication of bacteria. The existence of bacteria has been established for the most ancient periods in the history of the earth.[12] L. Cayeux has shown that the oolithic rocks of Minnesota include numberless bacteria, as also do the Archaean schists of British Columbia, Montana and France, and the Pre-Cambrian rocks of Calvados. Morphologically these fossil bacteria are identical with those of the present.

(ii) *Other "living fossils"*: Today it is known that it is not only Protista which are capable of persisting so: examples have

---

[12] I.e. the Pre-Cambrian. The corresponding geological formations are called Archaean when they have been metamorphosed and Algonquin or Pre-Cambrian when they have not.

been found among metaphyta and metazoa. G. G. Simpson[13] mentions some of these cases of what he calls "low-rate lines":

Lingulids, Ordovician to Recent; limulids, Triassic to Recent; coelacanths, Devonian to Recent (the lately discovered *Latimeria*); sphenodonts, Triassic to Recent; crocodiles (*sensu stricto*), early Cretaceous to Recent; opossums, late Cretaceous to Recent. The list could be considerably extended. Those mentioned are a few of the so-called living fossils, groups that survive today and that show relatively little change since the very remote time when they first appeared in the fossil record. Besides other examples of the same sort, there are groups now extinct that were low-rate lines while they lasted, but a survey suggests that the number of these was relatively small—an observation that is important for this problem. It would also be legitimate to add a large number of groups that have become well-differentiated in a comparatively minor way, but that early acquired a fundamental structural type that has been relatively invariable; for instance: turtles, the group as a whole from the Triassic and several recent families and a few genera from the Cretaceous; bats, from the middle Eocene (at least); armadillos, from the upper Palaeocene; rabbits, from upper Eocene; whales, the order as a whole from the Eocene and modern families mostly from the Miocene.

This is not a complete list of all forms now living which have existed from the secondary or early tertiary periods. The case of a "living fossil" which excited most interest was the fairly recent discovery of the coelacanth. In 1938 a living coelacanth was fished up on the east coast of South Africa and studied by Professor J. L. B. Smith of Rhodes University, Grahamstown. On December 20th, 1952, a second—"of Anjouan"—was caught in the Comores archipelago and, like the first, studied by Professor Smith. Since then six others have been caught in the same area. The story has been told by Professor Smith himself in *Old Four-Legs: The Story of the Coelacanth*.[14] Let us here briefly note three reasons why the discovery was so important: the extreme antiquity of the coelacanth, its remark-

---

[13] *Tempo and Mode in Evolution*, pp. 125–6.
[14] London and New York, Longmans, 1956.

able stability, and the stage in evolution it represents. Let us quote Professor Smith:

> There is evidence that at the close of the Silurian period and over the beginning of the Devonian some striking change was at work, for it was then that fishes something like the modern types we know first appeared. They had true bony jaws and overlapping scales, and a skeleton at least partly bony. Their fins were peculiar, rather like small paddles with a fringe of soft rays, so that they were named "Crossopterygii" or "fringe-finned". These fishes represented a tremendous step forward in evolution in more ways than one. Not only did they at that very early stage show important features that have remained predominant in fish life to this day, but one group of them gave rise to forms that colonized the land and were indeed our own ancestors [p. 15].

> This is where the coelacanth comes into the picture. There were two main lines in the Crossopterygii, named Coelacanths and Rhipidistia. No one could fail to see, even from only fossil remains, how closely they were related. Because somewhat earlier fossils of the Rhipidistia than of Coelacanths are known, most scientists today hold the view that the Rhipidistia came first and that Coelacanths developed from them. Because this view was expressed by one or two leading workers, even without any really positive evidence, it is commonly held even today. If it were true, however, since all those forms lived under the same conditions, it is almost incredible that there should be no sign of transitional types. But in fact, there are the Rhipidistia, and there are the Coelacanths, and nothing in between. It is at least as likely that both of these types came from some as yet unknown common ancestral form, and that form would be ancestral to man as well [p. 17].

> This remarkable type appeared much more than 300 million years ago, and has gone on, virtually unchanged as such things go, until the present time. In that long time countless other types of fishy creatures evolved, flourished, and vanished, many of them types that may have seemed more suited for survival than our old Coelacanth, but he has outlived them all [pp. 20–1].

Let us conclude this rather sketchy review of the permanent features of the living world by suggesting that the general laws of life overrule the particular laws of evolutionary change. In other words, biological evolution cannot be thought of without the recognition of the permanence of those properties found in all living creatures whatever their degree of complexity. To speak of the "coming-to-be" of living creatures is to speak also of an unchanging stuff conserved under the ornaments of change.

CHAPTER IX

METAPHYSICS AND

EVOLUTION

THE POLEMICAL ATMOSPHERE OF EVOLUTIONARY THEORIES

Since the theory of evolution contends that man's origins are one with those of the animals it has always seemed to be opposed to the Scriptures and to Christianity, and to those religious philosophers who seek to interpret religious beliefs by the natural reason, following the Anselmian *fides quaerens intellectum*. Evolutionary theory thus developed in a polemical atmosphere, and its eddies have swirled over the dikes of scientific research proper to flood into the fields of revealed religion, of ethics, and even of politics. Even now we read in expositions of evolution frequent careful assurances by their authors that such and such terms they use, such as tendency, orthogenesis, and so on, do not have in their minds any mystical, metaphysical or supernatural overtones. This almost conventional precaution shows first that some scientists still suffer from an antireligious bias, and secondly that in their minds the idea of a relationship between science and metaphysics has not been quite eliminated. On the other hand there are some who seek, behind the natural phenomena which we apprehend by our senses and whose laws science studies, a fundamental Reason for their existence. These are men who are not content to explore the world of sensible experience only, but take flight in thought towards an invisible world.

They are commonly lumped together somewhat pityingly with the metaphysicians; some have even gone so far as to deny their right to seek such a supreme truth. But in fact, metaphysical inquiry, of which Auguste Comte spoke as already dead, has survived more than a century of astonishing progress in science, which suggests that it may be a constant human phenomenon.

A good many confusions, however, still surround this whole question; in the pages that follow we shall try to resolve some of these.

NATURAL SCIENCE

The positive disciplines concerned in evolutionary theorizing are the natural sciences: astronomy, physics, chemistry and biology. ("Positive" here must not be confused with "positivist", which refers to a philosophical school of thought.) The natural sciences, investigating the sensible world, demand the use of principles of explanation themselves taken from nature. Nature, that is, the sidereal universe, the earth, and the living beings which inhabit it, is understood in the sense of a coherent body of phenomena which determine one another in accordance with physical laws gradually being discovered by science. Scientists do not shrink from saying that nature is intelligible; that is, there is a conformity of natural things to our intelligence. This conformity, when scientific knowledge is carried far enough, confers two powers on man, the first in the intellectual order, prediction, the second in the pragmatic order, control of nature.

In the first case, the knowledge of certain laws of nature allows the prediction of some still unknown fact or facts, and the inclusion of these in our picture of the sensible world (for example, the existence of the planet Neptune announced on August 1st, 1846, by Le Verrier and actually found by Gall on September 23rd of the same year). In the second case, science furnishes man with the means of acting on nature, to some degree at any rate. Recently a great operation, the International Geophysical Year, has been planned and carried through in regard to this planet Earth in particular, to the exclusion of the other heavenly bodies. Positive scientific method, as it has been adopted and used for two hundred years, is deliberately restricted to the investigation of mechanical causality in the universe, and it cuts out of its explanations causes which do not fall within the scope of the measurable parameters of space and time. The favourable prejudice with which it is generally regarded has not been without its influence in its successful application in various fields; we shall examine the consequences of this prejudice later. In the meantime, from the methodological viewpoint, we may consider positive research limited to the spatio-temporal world justifiable, such research excluding, if not as of right at any rate by convention, all reference to factors outside that world.

THE METAPHYSICAL DIMENSION OF THE HUMAN MIND

Now despite this it remains true that the mind of man generally, including that of the laboratory scientist, contains, whether he wishes it or not, a field much more extensive than the spatio-temporal world. This has the effect of leaving him with a feeling of dissatisfaction, even when explanation by natural causes is pushed as far as possible. Now, if we get back to the story of the last century and a half of evolutionary theory, we see straight away that most of the scientists who have been concerned in its as yet incomplete construction have introduced into it, consciously or not, metaphysical considerations, simply because the human mind is not divided into water-tight compartments. The mind of the scientist at work in his laboratory, at his bench, is never completely virgin, never a *tabula rasa*. It is that of a man who already has a personality of his own, his own past. He is the subject of various psychological impressions to which he reacts, by way of acceptance, rejection, or hesitation. In short, he possesses, whether he likes it or not, a minimum of beliefs, positive or negative or uncertain, concerning the meaning of life. Moreover, the fact that he belongs to society forces him to make choices every day which frequently involve extra-scientific issues; for example, they may be moral decisions. In other words, the scientist is not, in his daily life, quite independent of an atmosphere which affects him and of which he must take account whether willingly or unwillingly. There are no pure mathematicians, pure physicists, pure biologists. There are men who study mathematics, physics, or biology, men whom these sciences would leave quite incapable of all social life if they never strayed beyond their bounds.

This idea that the human mind possesses a metaphysical dimension in its nature has been often expressed: and it is true. But some scientists come close to thinking that in getting rid of all metaphysical considerations they are undergoing a purification necessary to the success of their scientific work, and they carry their asceticism to the point of denying the legitimacy of any extra-scientific thinking. One wonders whether such censors have ever reflected on the foundations of human knowledge, of any kind at all.

POSITIVE SCIENCE HAS A METAPHYSICAL FOUNDATION

It may not be irrelevant to recall in passing that however buried science may be in the world of facts and phenomena accessible to our senses, thanks to a method adopted conventionally by all scientists, it is none the less true that even knowledge as far as possible purified of all transcendental factors rests on a postulate the metaphysical signification of which it is certainly difficult to deny. Actually the most positive science demands of the scientist the belief, a prerequisite of all research, in the "intelligibility of nature"; in other words, the belief that it is possible to attain to truth, a belief often confirmed by experimental proof. So great a physicist as Einstein, a stranger to all traditional religion, did not scruple when speaking of this subject to use words like "marvel", "miracle" and "mystical emotion". He once wrote: "The most beautiful emotion we can experience is the mystical. It is the sower of all true art and science.... To know that what is impenetrable to us really exists, manifesting itself as the highest wisdom and the most radiant beauty, ... this knowledge, this feeling, is at the centre of true religiousness. In this sense, and in this sense only, I belong to the ranks of devoutly religious men."[1]

"To the sphere of religion belongs the faith that the regulations valid for the world of existence are rational, that it is comprehensible to reason. I cannot conceive of a genuine scientist without that profound faith. The situation may be expressed by an image: science without religion is lame, religion without science is blind."[2]

What is said here about scientific knowledge applies equally to first philosophy or metaphysics, despite the radical difference in their objects. The principle of intelligibility is one of the axioms on which metaphysical reasoning is founded. In the end, all knowledge that is really worked out, whether its object is physical or metaphysical, has as its fundamental axiom the belief that our reason is an instrument of the truth.

There have always been scientists who have sought to attribute a purely empirical origin to this belief or intuition. In particular, they claim that it was the observation of the regularity of natural phenomena, for example, the courses of the stars, which suggested to the first men the idea of laws of nature. Yet the higher animals, who possess almost the same senses as ourselves, have never built any science. Beyond doubt sense-data are the basis of man's science. In animals these produce only biological reflexes, in man they produce biological reflexes—*and reflection*. Reflection is the fruit of the conceptual intelligence proper to man, and it is to this ruling faculty that he can ascribe the establishment of the regularities and the laws which are the germs of all our knowledge. We shall make our thought on this matter still clearer if we say that science, which seeks to formulate the laws of the sensible world, and metaphysics, which has as its object the world of

---

[1] Philipp Frank, *Einstein, his Life and Times*, London, 1948, pp. 340–1.

[2] *Op. cit.*, p. 343.

values and their source, arise from the same faculty, which is to many a mystery, the natural light of the human reason.

METAPHYSICS, SCIENCE AND EVOLUTION

As compared with the metaphysicians, defined as seekers of first causes and first principles, men who investigate the natural sciences behave in many different ways, which is reflected and actualized in a number of systems of ideas. We shall here mention positivism or agnosticism; materialism; and spiritism; and note straight away that each of these doctrines includes various shades of opinion.

Positivism or agnosticism

When one speaks of positivism or agnosticism, one immediately thinks of Auguste Comte. But this philosopher was preceded by Condorcet and the school of Saint-Simon, and followed by Littré. English positivism goes back to David Hume in the eighteenth century and to John Stuart Mill, Herbert Spencer and T. H. Huxley in the nineteenth. Ernst Mach was the spokesman of positivism in Central Europe in the latter half of the nineteenth century. Let us quote a few passages from Émile Littré which sum up clearly the principles of positivist agnosticism.[3]

> The cosmogonies found at the beginnings of the writings of the ancient religions cannot stand up to the criticism which experimental science daily brings against them, even without wanting to. The place they held is from now on an empty place. Positive cosmogonies fill it, perhaps, but not because they claim —nor have they the power—to penetrate the absolute and grasp first and final causes; they do however open up sufficiently wide views in space and time for it to be possible to reach the limits of what is possible to our knowledge as of what is possible to our sight. Positive cosmogonies have the supreme advantage of marking clearly the dividing line between the finite and the infinite, between the known and the unknowable. They also have this characteristic, that they cut out altogether the supernatural. They would dissolve at once if the supernatural were

[3] *La Science au point de vue philosophique*, Paris, Didier, 1873.

allowed to seep in through some small crack. Why is this, and where does this incompatibility between science and the supernatural come from? From the relativity of the human mind itself.[4] The subjective and *a priori* power of conception can surely create and combine all the absolutes it can envisage; but when these absolutes come outside the subjective isolation in which they were born, then the human mind, relative as it is, intervenes and recognizes only what is relative like itself. The learning of this fact of relativity has taken a long time to be achieved, but now it is done, and science is now certain that she can only attain knowledge of what is included in the succession of natural causes. (*Op. cit.*, pp. 559–60.)

From this text we can infer that positivism limits scientific knowledge to natural causes—we could say, to the relations between phenomena which are spatio-temporal and accessible to our senses or instrumental extensions of them; all scientists, whatever their philosophical opinions, are agreed on this and that it cuts out as unknowable by scientific knowledge any principle which transcends the physical world; "positive science claims that it denies no such principle, nor affirms any" (*op. cit.*, p. 562).

On these principles, positivism is opposed both to materialism and to theology:

When positivism hears the materialist proclaiming that life is the result of known chemical and physical forces, she refuses to accept a solution that goes beyond the evidence. But she does not reject the materialist solution in order to make room for the theological one: the action of a creative God is also unverifiable by experience and so suffers the same fate of being rejected. Now, if anyone asks positive philosophy what is her own answer, between the generation of the materialist and the theologian's supernatural creation, she replies that she has no solution to offer, that nothing can make her believe what is not demonstrably true, and that she accepts, with as much firmness as humility, an invincible ignorance of all that is undemonstrable. (*Op. cit.*, p. 542.)

[4] The relativity of the human mind is the limitation of its capacity for knowledge which is recognized by everyone, even the spiritist philosophers (author's note).

Materialism or monism

Materialism or monism is generally a fighting doctrine, firmly anti-spiritist. In its own way, materialism is a metaphysical theory that affirms an absolute, that of matter-energy, which it claims is the sole source of all phenomena, including that of mind. This monist conception postulates the eternity of matter. Joined with the idea of evolution it sometimes leads its supporters to put back into circulation the ancient myth of the Eternal wheel or Great Year (760,000 years according to Plato) which takes the form today of cycles of development of the universe which succeed one another, last a very long time, and perpetually produce more cycles like themselves. Nietzsche, at the time when he conceived Zarathustra, expressed his delight at this representation. If there be joined to it, as is the case with some of our contemporaries, a nostalgia for the divine, they become pantheists. Pantheism finds itself unable to distinguish God from the sensible world; since it cannot separate Being from beings, it calls them the same thing. Once he has suppressed the transcendent and personal God of Genesis and the Gospel, the most a scientist can do is proclaim the immanence of God in nature and nature in God. Since this immanence is reciprocal such thinking arrives at the conclusion that all the phenomena of the universe are to be attributed to one and only one substance. Haeckel, in his *Riddle of the Universe*, says that the idea of God is the same as that of nature or substance, and that therefore pantheism is necessarily the point of view of modern natural science.

Spiritism

Spiritism has its firmest roots in the Judaeo-Christian tradition and the religions branching from it. Spiritist metaphysics, like the scriptures on which it depends, and in opposition to materialism and the pantheist conception, professes a primary and radical dualism: for a rigid distinction is drawn between the Creator, the first Cause of all that exists, and the creation of our sensible universe. This sensible universe, or world of bodies, animate or inanimate, is subordinated to God, the absolute Being, non-temporal and unextended. On the nature of man, spiritism divides into two schools in the main:

(i) The *idealist* school maintains that man is endowed with a spiritual soul quite distinct from his body. (Plato, St Augustine, Descartes.)

(ii) The *realist* or *hylomorphist* school holds that human substance is a unity, but a composite unity. Man is formed of two principles, each incomplete but complementary to the other: the spiritual soul or form, and the body or matter. (Aristotle, St Thomas Aquinas, and Catholic theology generally.)

We shall return later to these brief summaries. But we can see already, if we discount agnosticism or positivism, which, while not denying the existence of the supernatural, yet declares it inaccessible to the human mind, that there is a metaphysical conflict between materialism and spiritism which still affects evolutionary theory. We shall make the points of friction plainer in the next chapter.

CHAPTER X

EVOLUTION AND

CHRISTIANITY

CATHOLIC INTELLECTUAL CIRCLES AND EVOLUTION

In 1945 the prehistorian Count Begouen published a pamphlet[1] in which he gathered together some personal memories of stages in the story of the tension between evolutionary and Christian thought. This work coming from a Catholic scientist is interesting because it tells without bitterness part of the ideological history of evolution, which it would be fascinating to write more fully. Here we shall simply fasten upon one obvious fact: there are now, to oversimplify, two kinds of evolutionists, philosophically speaking: atheists and believers. In the second class are included Catholic scientists of great renown, lay or religious; the list would be impressive. From this last fact we can infer that, contrary to what some people think, they have not been prevented from carrying on their research or from publishing their results.

As we have tried to show earlier, the theory of biological evolution contains at present too many gaps and uncertainties to impose itself on every mind as an absolutely coherent whole. All the same, Catholic evolutionists who have felt entitled to disregard the gaps in the scientific information and declare

---

[1] *Quelques souvenirs sur le mouvement des idées transformistes dans les milieux catholiques; suivi de la mentalité spiritualiste des premiers hommes*, Paris, Bloud et Gay, 1945.

their faith in the evolutionary hypothesis ought to show how they manage to justify their double allegiance. We shall not here contradict a saying of Fr Teilhard de Chardin's quoted by Count Begouen[2]: "There should be no doubt about the correct attitude for the believer. He need only inquire into both sides patiently and confidently. Faith guarantees that he will find no contradiction between his *credo* and his human knowledge." But this happy state of affairs is not always realized in practice.

Thus, the Teaching of the Church leaves the doctrine of Evolution an open question, as long as it confines its speculations to the development, from other living matter already in existence, of the human body. (That souls are immediately created by God is a view which the Catholic faith imposes on us.) In the present state of scientific and theological opinion, this question may be legitimately canvassed by research, and by discussion between experts on both sides. At the same time, the reasons for and against either view must be weighed and adjudged with all seriousness, fairness and restraint; and there must be a readiness on all sides to accept the arbitrament of the Church, as being entrusted by Christ with the task of interpreting the Scriptures aright, and the duty of safeguarding the doctrines of the faith. There are some who take rash advantage of this liberty of debate, by treating the subject as if the whole matter were closed—as if the discoveries hitherto made, and the arguments based on them, were sufficiently certain to prove, beyond doubt, the development of the human body from other living matter already in existence. They forget, too, that there are certain references to the subject in the sources of divine revelation, which call for the greatest caution and prudence in discussing it.[3]

This caution and prudence are all the more necessary to Catholic evolutionists because on the scientific level the doctrine of biological evolution still raises a thousand difficulties, and also because on the ontological level they have to take account of the philosophy "which the Church recognizes

---

[2] *Op. cit.*, p. 41.

[3] Encyclical of Pius XII, *Humani generis*, August, 1950, § 36. (English trans. by Mgr Ronald A. Knox, Catholic Truth Society, 1957.)

and receives. It upholds the real, genuine validity of human thought-processes; it upholds the unassailable principles of metaphysics—sufficient reason, causality and finality; it upholds the possibility of arriving at certain and unalterable truth."[4] Now this philosophy, which sets out to justify the truths of faith by the natural reason, is altogether opposed to that monist, materialist philosophy under whose auspices the theory of evolution has been developed.

PHILOSOPHICAL ANTINOMIES WITHIN THE THEORY OF EVOLUTION ITSELF

In 1899, in the first chapter of *The Riddle of the Universe*, E. Haeckel stated the dualist-monist opposition clearly in this way:

> From the point of view of a contemporary natural scientist, the various movements in philosophy fall into two opposing groups: on the one side, dualism—the realm of division, and on the other, monism—the realm of unity. Teleological and idealist doctrines generally attach themselves to the former group, realist and mechanistic ones to the latter. Dualism (in the widest sense!) separates in the universe two absolutely different substances, a material world and an immaterial God who is set over against it as its creator, its conserver, and its governor. On the other hand monism (also in the widest sense of the word!) recognizes in the universe but one unique substance, which is at once "God and Nature"; for monism, body and spirit (or matter and energy) are strictly one and the same. The super-terrestrial God of dualism necessarily leads us to theism; the intracosmic god of the monist, on the other hand, to pantheism.... We ourselves hold firmly to pure monism, the unambiguous pure monism of Spinoza: matter, as a substance indefinitely extended, and spirit or energy, as a substance which feels and thinks, are the two fundamental attributes, the two essential properties, of the divine cosmic Being which embraces all the universal substance.

These statements enable us to draw up a table summarizing the principal antinomies which come to the surface when the

[4] *Humani generis*, § 29.

monist and dualist[5] theories are set against one another within the framework of their relations with the theory of evolution.

MONISM	DUALISM
1. Does not recognize a personal ultramundane God.	Posits the existence of a personal ultramundane God.
2. All the phenomena of the universe are determined by the evolutive properties of matter-energy, which is eternal. Being eternal, it has neither beginning nor end. It thus represents the sole absolute that the scientist has to take into consideration.	Matter-energy is not eternal. It was created *ex nihilo* by a personal God. The four-dimensional universe which we know had a beginning and will have an end.
3. Our present universe in its three aspects — mineral, biological, and human—is the result of an Evolution, change being the universal law of the universal substance, or matter-energy.	Our present universe is, at least in very great measure, the result of an Evolution. But beside the evolutive processes room must be made in the theory for the phenomena of permanence.
4. Man is the last-born of the order of primates, the representatives of which are genealogically linked.	Man possesses the general biological characters of the primates, and more especially those of the anthropomorphs or anthropoids.
5. "The human soul is not, any more than that of any higher animal, an immaterial, independent substance, but a collective term denoting a sum of cerebral functions; these are conditioned, like all other vital functions, by physical and chemical processes, these last being themselves also subordinate to the law of substance" (Haeckel, *op. cit.*).	According to the realist or hylomorphic philosophy commonly admitted by the Church, man is a unique substance, human substance, compound of two principles, each incomplete without the other, but complementary: the substantial form, or spiritual soul, and the matter, or body. The spirit, as the substantial form, determines the matter of the body, and is to a certain degree determined by it.

[5] We are dealing here with realist dualism, which is the philosophy commonly admitted by the Church, and leave idealist dualism out of consideration.

6. The human soul is the integrated ensemble of nervous functions. As these can be explained by physics and chemistry, they disappear with death; this is essentially decomposition, a return from heterogeneous to homogeneous (from a living to a mineral state).

The human soul (spiritual) is during life incorporated in matter. After death, the decomposition of the matter of the body (its return to the mineral state) leaves in existence the active intellect, which is immaterial and for that very reason preserved from the changes which matter-energy undergoes.

7. The concept of eternal matter-energy excludes all forms of purposiveness.

The concept of creation implies that of purpose.

This list of antinomies is by no means complete, but it is enough to show that for the philosopher there is a real contradiction between monist and dualist evolutionary theory. We might also wonder whether Christian evolutionists have succeeded in resolving all the difficulties their adversaries throw up against them. I know that all Christians are supposed to subscribe to the general ideas of a personal God, and creation *ex nihilo*, and hence of purposiveness. But up to the present none of these evolutionists seems to have escaped from the looseness of thought that consists in attributing to the properties of matter-energy all the phenomena of life, and in particular human thought, which raises the problem of the immortality of the soul. This is, unless I am mistaken, the crucial point in their difficulties. And it is in examining the problem of man as a spiritual being from various angles that we hope to disentangle the confusions that surround it at present.

MAN AS SPIRIT

We shall take from Fr Teilhard de Chardin's *Le Phénomène humain*, since he is the most prominent of Christian evolutionists, the following remarks: "Has science ever taken the trouble to look at the world otherwise than by means of the outsides of things? If we do make the effort to consider in a given case of a phenomenon, the *whole* phenomenon, we are bound in the case of the human phenomenon to agree that there exists in man an 'interior', reflective consciousness, which 'is the object of a direct intuition and the stuff of all knowledge'."

This is a valid starting-point. But are we entitled to postulate that this consciousness which appears clearly with man "has cosmic extension, and as such spreads out indefinitely in space and time", and to add: "Without any argument being possible, there appears by a sort of tearing apart an 'interior' at the heart of things, in the depths of ourselves. So much so that to one degree or another this 'interior' clearly exists everywhere in nature and always has existed. Since at any point in itself the stuff of the universe has an internal face, it is necessarily biface in its structure; biface, that is, just as much as granular, in every region of space and time. Co-extensive with their outside, there is an inside in things."

How ought we to conceive this inside of things? Are we not to fear that in the mind of the reader there will arise the idea that the "reflective step" in man is only a simple effect of emergence? In truth, the constant recourse to the "great biological law of complication", which is bound to "a correlative growth of interiorization, that is, of *psyche* or consciousness", seems to lead to an idea of a genesis of mind (noögenesis) considered as a phenomenon of nature which suddenly occurs as a development of the stuff of the universe: "mind emerging (by a pancosmic operation) from the *materia-matrix*, matter."[6]

Since Fr Teilhard's method was avowedly phenomenological we clearly cannot refuse him the right to postulate a correlation between the most complex brain, that of man, and "the reflective step"—a correlation admitted by everyone—but we have the impression that with him this correlation wears an aspect of material causality. I know that he is speaking from a phenomenological point of view when he says that at this level "consciousness presents itself and asks to be treated not as a particular and subsistant entity but as an 'effect', as 'the specific effect of complication' ". I also know that from this starting-

[6] Letter to Mme Maryse Choisy of March 13th, 1954, in *Psyche*, No. 99–100, January–February, 1955.

point he is making an important point in favour of metaphysics. But still we have not got rid of all equivocation. For
in saying also that "consciousness" is being taken in its most
general sense, to denote every kind of psychic phenomenon,
from the most rudimentary forms of internal perception conceivable to humanity, he exposes himself to the reproach of
having taken sides with panpsychism and returned to a
hylozoist conception which it would be very difficult to
persuade modern physicists to admit.

The doctrine of creation makes it logically necessary for us
to attribute to the physical properties of the physico-chemical
elements of the mineral world a prospective potentiality of
divine origin. But these determinate properties which analytical
chemistry discovers in matter have nothing to do with a
consciousness which is supposed to be immanent in the
mineral state. When Fr Teilhard writes that "by the very indi-
vidualization of our planet a certain mass of consciousness was
trapped in the beginning in terrestrial matter", he proposes to
us an idea which we cannot admit in its bald form as he puts it.
It is true that the universe, in all its parts and in the totality of
its phenomena, appears to us as the expression of a majestic
Mind. This is why it is, to some degree, intelligible to us, because the human mind possesses the ability to assimilate whatever in things is connatural with it. But to speak of a certain
mass of *consciousness* in the beginning is to use irreconcilable
terms: *mass* is a physical quantity; *consciousness*, even in the
beginning (we shall return to this point), is a datum of
psychology quite foreign to physics.

IMMANENCE AND TRANSCENDENCE

Beneath these considerations lie the problems, fundamental
for evolutionary philosophy, of immanence and transcendence.
These words are not always used in an unambiguous way, and
hence there arise a number of confusions we must straighten
out. First we shall distinguish, with the scholastics, immanent
action from transitive action, which characterize respectively
living and non-living things. The transitive action of mineral

bodies serves for us as a parameter for the study of the immanent action of living things.

Transitive action

Inanimate objects only possess the capacity for transitive action: that is, they cannot act except on bodies other than themselves: one stone hitting another sets that other moving. In this example the movement of the first stone does not stay in itself but is *transferred* to the second stone, presupposed at rest. In inorganic chemistry, the action of one substance on another involves the *transformation* of the two substances. The identities of the two original substances disappear, by a reciprocal, transitive action.

Immanent action

Immanent activity *remains in* (Latin *immanere*) the subject in which it comes into being. It can be defined as the totality of factors which maintain for a certain time the identity of a determinate living thing. Xavier Bichat, when he said of life that it was "the totality of factors which resist death", was not far off—probably without realizing it—the scholastic conception of immanent activity. The idea of immanent action is not a theoretical concept devoid of empirical sense; it corresponds to a *fact* the conditions and consequences of which are known experimentally. We know quite well how, by what mechanical means, the temporal integrity of living things is achieved and maintained before their final dissolution. The physico-chemical factors of varying degrees of complexity which come into play in the phenomena of life are of the same nature as those of the mineral world, but, as we mentioned earlier (Chapter II), they only need and use a certain number of the natural chemical elements. In this fact itself, the phenomena of life already represent something new compared with the inorganic world. Another new feature of life is the raising of the "biogenic" elements, so to speak, to extremely complex forms; for example, protein molecules, and others, which are in their turn the basic elements of living tissues. I have often used the

word "upgrading" (which is opposed to "degrading") to denote
the ascent in rank (or increase in physico-chemical complexity)
which characterizes living things. There is no doubt that this
ascent can be scientifically explained. It has become trite to
say that life appeared when its proper physico-chemical conditions were realized. But one could say as much of crystalline
rocks. What is often left out of the scientific explanation of life
is the *direction* of immanent action. Now, this direction is
obvious: the end or aim of immanent action is in the living
thing itself. Once again, we are dealing with a fact the biologist
can study with the help of physico-chemical parameters, without appealing to metaphysical considerations.

But, to be precise, the scientific comparison of the
phenomena of the inorganic and of the organic worlds brings
to light in the latter a significant difference. To whatever level
on the biological scale it belongs, the living thing appears to
the observer as a machine whose functioning results in its own
conservation (for a time) and its reproduction, which conserves
the species of which it is a member (for an indefinite period).
Up to now we have not left the realm of positive science, and
are considering the living thing as a machine, a very complex
machine, it is true, but one whose "works" we are getting to
know better and better. Our knowledge has reached the point
where the scientist can interfere in the functioning of these
machines, and we can glimpse the moment when it will be
possible for him to build from all its parts an artificial living
thing. Suppose this marvel accomplished by some biochemist,
there will still be this difference between the living machine,
natural or artificial, and the industrial machine: the essential
difference that the former will function for itself—in other
words its action will be immanent; but the latter will only
function in relation to some end external to itself according to
the model of transitive action.

We are thus led to wonder what is the secret of immanent
action. It appears to us the more mysterious because it is the
source of living nature; the world of life is an astonishing
phenomenon, and the more a scientist learns about it the

greater is his sense of wonder. Let us be quite clear that the first men were the possessors, without having asked for it or earned it in any way, of this wonderful inheritance, which was established before they came on to the scene, and compared with which their first artefacts were but the poor toys of a child. Look for a moment at this marvellous world, brought into being quite independently of man, who contemplates it and uses it, who depends on it in part, on the mineral world from which he takes his basic elements, but who rearranges these in novel configurations which, in the context of the external environment, serve him in such a way as to realize the *autonomy of the living being*.[7] At this point we have reached this conclusion: that the autonomy of the living being is brought about by immanent action, which is realized by various mechanisms joined one to another in such a way as to make each living thing a machine which works for its own ends.

Let us again insist on the difference between an industrial machine and a living one. The former is conceived and constructed by man; he supplies it with the energy it needs and the matter which it has to transform; he receives from it the product he intended to get. The living machine is brought forth naturally; it constructs itself, beginning from a pre-existent living thing; it feeds itself; it functions in order to preserve itself and to ensure the preservation of its species; and all these operations may be quite unconscious. This brief comparison of the living thing with an industrial machine enables us to refer the construction and operation of the latter to a human *psyche*, which surely has nothing to do with natural productions, and especially life. But men have for long been struck by the fact that natural mechanisms are far more powerful and far more complicated than those which they can construct themselves, and have inferred that the universe bears the mark of Intelligence. Hence the ideas of a world-soul and of creation which are opposed to one another today in the debates about

[7] The autonomy of the living being is clearly not absolute; it is relative to the conditions of the environment, which it to a great extent dominates.

evolutionary theory. To keep within the terms of our argument, which began from the notion of immanent action, we shall try to make clear the different ways in which the words "immanent" and "immanence" are used in practice.

The idea of immanence

We have insisted earlier that *immanent action* is not just a speculative idea but a positive fact. The adjective "immanent" and the noun "immanence" have different meanings in different contexts, however, and to kill two birds with one stone and to make our argument as concrete as possible, we shall discuss as an example the different kinds or levels of *psyche*. We have said that living things, even the least complicated, enjoy a relative autonomy which is bound up with the characteristic phenomenon of immanent action. This has often been explained, since Aristotle, by a reality more or less distinct from the body called the soul or *psyche*. Many scientists and philosophers both of antiquity and of modern times have explained the phenomena of life by reference to the *psyche*, thus setting in relief the characteristic quality of intelligence which scientific analysis finds in the dispositions of the living machine.

The vegetative soul

Obviously Aristotle knew nothing of the microscopic members of the world of life, but what he knew about plants enabled him to form the idea of the vegetative soul, corresponding to the functions of nutrition, growth and production. Now in plants these functions are of a purely mechanical nature. They are bound up in a chain of determinate events the discovery of which is the object of science and which cuts out of the world of plants what we call consciousness. A tree, or any plant whatever, *vegetates* in a completely unconscious manner; that is, without having any knowledge of the changes which it undergoes. The same is true of those microscopic creatures which it is often difficult to place either in the animal or in the plant kingdom; many Protista never pass the level of the un-conscious, vegetative *psyche*.

The animal soul

Sensations and sensibility appear with animals which are slightly more complicated. It is difficult to say of some uni-cellular creatures which react to stimuli by movement whether they can be considered as the forerunners of higher animals which have a nervous system. One of the protozoa, however, such as Paramecium, can be said to be capable of reacting in some conditions in a way which conduces to its physiological optimum. But we need not suppose from the way it behaves that it is endowed with perceptive knowledge or subjectivity. It uses no external condition as a *sign* to be understood or interpreted; it only reacts to certain effective stimuli; still less does it appear to take such cognizance of the world apart from itself as to need to conceive *itself* as opposed to that world. Having no such knowledge, it does not *know* its ends, it merely *attains* them. Yet although none of its movements is consciously directed to an end, their totality nevertheless constitutes an orientated behaviour important for the life of the animal. In short there is here no purposive consciousness but only the working of a mechanism which suggests the elements of in-telligent behaviour and, as does all mechanism, purpose.

With the metazoa, which have a nervous system, we may properly speak of sensibility and sensations. A sensation, in the most general physiological sense of the word, is the effect produced in the nervous system by agents (stimuli) the activity of which has its effect through either the external environment or the internal, through internal organs. For there to be a sensation there must be: (1) an external or internal stimulus; (2) a receptor suited to the stimulus; (3) nervous centres which register it and, if the case demands it, transform it into reac-tion. Whatever their origin, sensations may or may not rise above the threshold of consciousness. Conscious sensation is first a kind of knowledge of the object which causes the nervous excitation. It distinguishes this object more or less clearly from any other, and confers on it a certain position in space. It includes, therefore, a cognitive or significative content. Moreover, a conscious sensation possesses almost necessarily an affective aspect, agreeable or disagreeable: it causes pleasure or pain; sometimes, however, this affective aspect is lacking and the sensation then merely provides information. Like conscious sensation, unconscious sensation is first of all a change in the nervous system, but this change may be registered or give rise to a reaction without involving affective or significative phenomena. For example, in the normal living thing the uneventful occurrence of most of the vegetative phenomena is linked with sensations of this kind.

The human psyche

Introspection on the one hand, and the objective study of human behaviour and its consequences in the living world on the other, lead to the affirmation that the human *psyche* ("soul" in the context of "human" has another meaning) transcends, in a purely descriptive and scientific sense, the animal's, which is bound to the particular, individual sensation and image. The philosophical analysis of the power of getting at things by their *ideas*, that is, by their general characters, by universals, and of the results of this power on the higher levels of knowledge, of action, of creation, by the apprehension of truth and ethical and aesthetic values, leads us to think of noögenesis as transcending (in the full sense) biological evolution; in other words the human *psyche* is clearly fundamentally irreducible to any imaginable arrangement of purely material elements. Let us briefly examine this problem in the light of the theory of the origins of man.

THE PROBLEM OF THE TRANSCENDENCE OF THE HUMAN MIND

The problem of the human mind and the logical difficulties associated with it arise immediately the question of the origins of man is tackled strictly on materialist lines. Some scientists, generally mechanistic, say or imply that the human mind is only an emergence of the organization of the nervous system.[8] All of a sudden, an advance at once quantitative and qualitative (structural) followed some mutation, and more came from less, so to speak. In the particular case of man, this previously unknown thing, reflection, extended the animal *psyche*: the birth of intelligence is simply due to the development of a heavier and more complex brain. We may reasonably wonder whether this newly-acquired property, the reason, with all its powers, is a simple emergence; for from the point of view of his fundamental composition, man is no different from the other primates, and reflective thought, articulate language and the power of invention are difficult to explain by simple growth and increased complexity of the nervous system. This is a stumbling-block for Christian evolutionists. Those who like Fr Teilhard de Chardin take a purely phenomenological attitude might well devote many brilliant pages to *the reflective step*. But they must agree that their position is by no means secure in everyone's eyes. Fr Teilhard says that the spiritist thinkers are right when they uphold so vehemently a certain transcendence of man over the rest of nature. But the materialists are no less right when they hold that man is only the last term in the series of animals. In this case, he maintains, as in so many others, the antithesis is resolved dynamically, in a movement—provided that an essential part in this movement be played by the completely natural phenomenon of "change of state". From the single cell to the thinking animal, as from the atom to the cell, the same process (the fermentation or concentration of the *psyche*) goes on continuously without a break, in the same direction. But, strictly

[8] Professor Cuénot uses the word emergence (or *novation*) to denote the appearance in orthogenetic series of organs new to the phylum. Some scientists or natural philosophers denote by "emergence" the appearance of properties in a synthesis of elements which are new in that the properties of the individual elements are different. The term "emergence", which seems to have been first used by Lewes (*Problems of Life and Mind*, vol. 1, p. 412, 1874), was used especially by Lloyd Morgan and S. Alexander, in a sense which puts it in fact in the very ancient tradition of emanation.

because of the continuous nature of this process, it is inevitable from the point of view of the *psyche* that certain sudden shifts should abruptly change the subject of its development.

I pass over all the difficulties that strict phenomenology raises with regard to Christian philosophy. They certainly did not escape Fr Teilhard: the birth of Thought, he says, like the first appearance of life, appears to us as a break in continuity. But in virtue of the limitations imposed on our sensible knowledge by the interplay of spatio-temporal series, it seems to be only in certain critical *phenomena* that we can in our experience grasp the reflective step which brought man, and man's mind, into being. But, this said, nothing prevents the spiritist thinker, for reasons of a higher order and at a further stage in his argument, postulating beneath the veil of phenomena which mark a revolutionary transformation such and such a "creative" act or such and such "special intervention", if he should want to. So writes Fr Teilhard, and it is quite certain that while such a position safeguards the principle of the transcendence of the mind, it runs the risk of reducing the spiritist thinker to the rôle of a "poor relation", *if* the only approach to the problem is that of scientific phenomenology, which, to be *precise*, it is not (for various reasons, some of which are derived from the conditions for the possibility and validity of human knowledge).[9]

Emergence, then, is a notion which may be valid and significant on the physico-chemical level, where it is certainly true that a *composite* body has properties different from those of its constituent parts; but already on that level—if the word "emergence" is not a magical formula, an "Open, Sesame!"— the philosophical problem of composition which we have

[9] It is probably important to say that the idea of the transcendence of the mind is based, from the point of view of traditional philosophy, on a critical analysis of the conditions of knowledge, an analysis which leads to an "ontology" of knowing, capable of resolving the classic problem of the subject-object relationship in quite a different way from that of Kant. (See, for example, *The Meaning of Existence; a Metaphysical Enquiry*, by Dom Mark Pontifex and Dom Illtyd Trethowan, London, Longmans, 1953.—*Trans.*)

already briefly mentioned arises. But what we want to stress now about the emergence of new properties from a synthesis of chemical elements—whether that synthesis is natural or artificial—is the fact that these new properties are still chemical properties. The change is not a change of the *nature* or *essence* of the elements involved in the compound.

Some biologists use the idea of emergence in an ambiguous way. When Georges Matisse[10] writes that *combination is creative* and that "arrangement, structure, composition, order —in space as well as in time—cause new properties to arise which are not in any of the elements assembled haphazardly in an uncoordinated mass", we are completely in agreement on the birth of new properties. But in the case of chemical things, the new properties which result from a combination of elements may be different from those of the elements themselves: it does not matter, for they still belong to the category of chemical phenomena, they are still essentially chemical.

The result of all this is that the "principle of emergence" (like the equivalent principles which dialectical materialism proposes),[11] so far from making possible the reduction by an unambiguous mechanism of all "differences of nature" to "differences of degree of complexity", on the contrary presupposes identity of nature, and thus assumes precisely what is in question. Now one sometimes has the impression, reading some Christian evolutionists, that they are afraid of falling short of what F. Meyer calls "intellectual stature", which he takes, it appears, in a rationalist sense to exclude all metaphysical explanation of experience. We have already said, and it is a fact of experience, that the human mind tends naturally to form the idea of a supra-sensible reality. It is undeniable that, set in opposition to the conventional and methodological limits of positive science, metaphysics may appear as a logical disgrace to some thinkers. It is also a fact that the rash use of

[10] *Monde vivant, monde minéral, et principe d'émergence*, Paris, Hermann, 1943.

[11] One of the first formulations of this principle seems to have been that of Friedrich Engels in *Herrn Eugen Dühring Umwälzung der Wissenschaft*.

metaphysical explanations has given rise to some regrettable blunders—and this is not only true of spiritist metaphysics. F. Meyer is right in saying that mechanists and vitalists face opposite ways, but he does not sufficiently acknowledge the legitimacy of a metaphysics which, without being mixed with positive science could, at the right moment, offer the latter a basis compatible with the requirements—with all the requirements—of reason. The fault of the Christian evolutionists we mentioned is that of adopting a purely phenomenological position without developing its ontological counterpart. It looks as though in their desire—their quite legitimate desire— to be regarded as true scientists, they leave on one side, temporarily at any rate, the requirements of Christian philosophy, and particularly the spirituality of the soul.

Let us recognize the difficulties in which the Christian evolutionists find themselves. On the scientific level they accept such doctrines as the animal origin of man, and they have to justify "the immediate creation of the soul by God". By adhering to the principles of evolutionary biology and the phenomenological method which they use, they find themselves in the awkward position of having to reserve a privileged place in nature for the human mind and its promised immortality. They do not doubt this privilege, it is true; they accept it. But they feel the weight of the scientific doctrine which prevents their faith from shining forth. If Christian evolutionists wish to remain faithful to their religious beliefs, they must at least justify the concept of creation *ex nihilo* and the immortality of the soul. This means that they must superimpose on their phenomenological explanation an ontological one.

If it is useless to look for a complete agreement between the Scriptures and science, one can nevertheless arrive at a rational explanation of religious beliefs by means of metaphysical reasoning, following the saying *fides quaerens intellectum*. It is true that, as Pascal said, metaphysical reasoning is "involved" and not suited to all minds, but when it comes to evolution, such reasoning ought to be examined by scientists, who are supposed to be representative users of conceptual intelligence. Some of them, of course, shirk positive metaphysics by a determined prejudice. But we can reasonably ask Christian evolutionists not to withdraw from the obligations imposed on them by their "trade mark".

We have seen that evolutionary theory is still far from gathering together on the scientific level all the data necessary to obtain general agreement. Suppose for a moment this problem solved, as do Christian evolutionists who admit, not without some heart burning, the doctrine of the descent of all living creatures and make it an article of belief, the question must then be asked, how can this belief fit in with the two ideas of the creation and the immortality of the soul? Christian evolutionists are not generally worried about the first. In fact, although most of the time they avoid discussing the question of absolute beginnings, they sometimes fall back on the opinion of some of the Fathers of the Church such as St Augustine, who looked upon the creation not as the sudden and simultaneous formation of all natural things but as the progressive development of the effects of creative Thought. Briefly, this means thinking of the creation not simply as an *act* calling into (and maintaining in) existence a collection of contingent beings, but equally as a project the implications of which show themselves progressively in the evolution of this collection of beings in time. On the second point, some Catholic scientists take the line of considering the appearance of man as a natural emergence of an autonomous evolution that continually grows more complex. This idea has the support of a number of arguments taken from general biology and in particular from neurophysiology. It is no achievement of modern science to say that the mind of man is bound up with a brain larger than and more complex than those of the anthropoids: did not Alcmaeon of Croton (*c.* 500 B.C.) say that the brain is the acropolis of the soul? On their side, have not Catholic philosophy and Catholic liturgy alike recognized the marvellous dignity of the human substance: *humanae substantiae dignitatem?*

It is possible to stay with the authentic Christian tradition in this matter of the human soul and its relations with the body, and its immortality promised to it by revelation, by sticking to hylomorphism, which interprets corporeal objects in terms of the two complementary concepts of matter and form, which do not constitute two separate modes of existence. Interpreted according to this philosophy, which is traditional in the Church, the human soul, in one way the "form" of the body (as the vegetative soul is of the plant or the sensitive soul is of the animal) and thereby a sort of natural extension of the series of pre-human forms, nevertheless transcends the body and those forms by reason of its intellectual principle (the active intellect or mind) which is capable of separate existence.

The evolutionist who is also a Christian must therefore say that if, phenomenologically regarded, the appearance of man is part of the story of evolution from infra-human forms, yet ontologically speaking, so far as concerns the subsistent intellectual principle, it must be independent of completely material determination, however complex the matter may become. From this point of view, to affirm that mind simply emerged by and from the increasing complication of the stuff of the universe, this being thought of as *fundamentally* constituted on the basis of physical or sensible "prime matter" (fundamental particles), is to contradict the belief in the spirituality and the immortality of the soul. The hypothesis which suggests, to avoid this contradiction, that physical "prime matter" has a (complementary) "biface" structure, taking up again in a different key the ancient tale of the "seminal reasons", seems to us philosophically dangerous and dialectically "evanescent", in Bergson's sense of the word.

CONCLUSION

The theory of evolution includes both certainties and un-certainties. Let us deal with cosmogony, biogenesis and anthropogenesis in turn.

COSMOGONY[1]

1. It looks as though the universe had a beginning (abso-lute?), since astro- and geo-physicists now have the means of finding out approximately the age of the stars and of the earth.

2. The stars are probably still being born, and in any case the heavenly bodies we can identify have not all the same age; the earth is as old as the galaxy, or nearly so.

3. The different physical states of the heavenly bodies sug-gest their transformation or evolution in time.

4. This evolution is very slow. For as long as man has looked at and described the heavens, he has been struck most by their unchanging appearance.

5. Modern astronomy and astrophysics suggest that the changes are so slow that they are imperceptible and an appearance of permanence results.

6. The different temperatures of the stars, which are all made of the same chemical elements, enable us to observe a physical evolution of the sidereal world, giving "evolution" here the meaning of temporal change.

BIOGENESIS

1. Since the phenomena of life cannot occur except within certain temperature limits, living things must have appeared at a particular stage in the physical evolution of the earth.

[1] We have not thought it necessary here to set out recent theories of the steady-state universe or the continual creation theory of Bondi, Hoyle, etc.

2. Constitutionally, living things are made from the same chemical elements as are found in the world, but the elements used to make up living bodies are fewer in number than those found in the physical world as a whole.

3. The elements used to make living bodies are always found as nucleoprotein macromolecules, which are made of nucleic acid and amino acids. These macromolecules have a power of utilizing their environment and are fundamental to the phenomena of assimilation and reproduction.

4. It is possible that biochemists will succeed in producing by artificial synthesis nucleoprotein macromolecules and others which go to make up living bodies, but it is at present unlikely that they will get from these molecules living things capable of subsisting and reproducing themselves.

5. Living things—Protista, plants, animals—can be classed in order of increasing complexity.

6. The present state of palaeontology shows that the living things with the highest degree of organization appeared most recently. To this fact is generally added the idea that the general direction of biological evolution is progressive (orthogenesis).

7. The theory of evolution sets out to explain biological evolution, in the general sense of the changes of the living world in the course of time, by means of the mechanism of inheritance. At first sight, this idea is simple and plausible. But its simplicity and facility seem to us incompatible with the difficulties of various kinds which it has not yet solved.

(a) Hereditary mechanisms only account for small changes in living things, on the level of the species, or at most of the family. At the present time, interfecundity is limited to members of the same species, and it is difficult to imagine that it was any different in the earlier history of life on the earth. It seems inconceivable that the progenitors of species with different kinds of organization should have been able to mate and, *a fortiori*, produce fertile crosses.

(b) Parthenogenetic mechanisms beginning from a ripe ovum that we now know of (by observation or experimentally), cannot give rise to supra-specific changes.

(c) The ingenious hypotheses of heterogenesis and paedomorphosis have as yet no experimental support. Thus there exists, between the general hypothesis of evolution and the data of observation and experiment in modern zoology, a gap which nothing at present seems able to fill, and the seriousness of which is enough to throw doubt on the claimed "fact" of evolution, of which even the palaeontological demonstration includes serious gaps in the material record.

8. The living world displays certain permanences, and especially general laws of life which overrule the particular laws of the evolution of living things.

ANTHROPOGENESIS

1. According to the palaeontological record bearing on the origin of man there are a series of phenotypes intermediate between present-day man and certain fossil primates.

2. This series, which grows in number as research progresses, probably justifies the inclusion of man in the line of animal evolution, though it does not strictly prove that inclusion.

3. For the great majority of present evolutionists all the representatives of the zoological group *homo* belong naturally together in the same family (monophyletism).

4. Neither palaeontology nor neo-zoology can bring forward any argument compelling adhesion to one or other of the three hypotheses—monogenism, polygenism, hologenism—concerning the number of individuals who first crossed the line dividing animal from man.

5. Supposing that this process of "making man" was achieved by means of a series of changes or progressive mutations of some size—or even by a mega-mutation enabling a sudden crossing of the dividing line (or area) to take place— palaeontology can only, in principle, expect to find the phenomenal, or more precisely phenotypic, correlative of those changes or mutations, just as it can only evaluate the importance of the change by its consequences in the material living world.

6. The intellect, by which man differs in his nature from the beasts, is not completely determined by matter and cannot result from an "emergence" at the end of an unambiguous evolution in complexity.[2]

7. The reality of the mind as subsistent form, even if it cannot be explained by means of purely material complexity, still does not require that the spiritual soul must necessarily have been the object of a special creative act which *breaks* the supposedly continuous phenomenological line of evolution.

[2] The increasing complexity of the stuff of the universe, on which Fr Teilhard de Chardin rightly insisted, might unfortunately be misinterpreted. It would be unacceptable if we had to understand it of *first* matter, in the sense of the ultimate physical or sensible reality (fundamental particles). It is no longer so if we take it as referring to *prime* matter or pure potentiality in the philosophical sense, and if the "emergence" of forms ordered according to their complexity is interpreted in the framework of hylomorphism.

SHORT GLOSSARY OF TECHNICAL TERMS

(Including all those marked * in the text)

Acaryota: elementary organisms with no nucleus, represented by viruses.

Acheulean: dressed stone industry the type of which was given by the implements (slender, flat axes; scrapers; arrow-heads, etc.) found in the alluvium at Saint-Acheul (Somme).

Allopolyploidy: multiplication of the number of chromosomes by crossing between species having different sets of chromosomes.

Amino-acids: relatively simple organic compounds containing both basic amino (NH_2) and organic acid (COOH) groups.

Amniotic sac: fluid-filled sac, within the uterus, in which the embryo of land-living vertebrates (reptiles, birds and mammals) develops, providing the necessary fluid environment.

Angstrom unit: unit of wavelength equal to one ten-millionth of a millimetre (10^{-8} cm.).

Anthropomorphs: catarrhine apes of fairly large size, with no tail, and semi-upright stance.

Arthropods: one of the chief and the largest phylum of the invertebrates; characterized by bilateral symmetry, segmented organization, paired articulated appendages (antennae, legs, etc.), an external skeleton of chitin (nitrogenous polysaccharide something like cellulose), etc. Includes crabs, insects, spiders, etc.

Australopithecines: fossil primates of para-hominid type from South Africa, with a cranial capacity of between 450 and 750 cc., distinguished from the anthropomorphs by their upright stature and a marked reduction in their canines.

Autotrophic: organisms (e.g., plants containing chlorophyll) which, by absorbing the light energy from the sun, can synthesize their own organic material constituents from purely inorganic matter, so that they are independent of organic matter outside themselves.

Bacteriophage: a virus that destroys bacteria.

Biotope: see p. 99.

Bradytelic: showing a slow rate of change.

Catarrhine: Old-world anthropoids characterized by a narrow nasal septum, a non-prehensile tail (when there is one), and a menstrual cycle; e.g. baboons, chimpanzees and men.

Chellean: dressed stone industry first described at Chelles (Seine-et-Marne) and characterized by sharp bifaced borders.

Chromosome: thread-like body numbers of which occur in the nucleus of every cell, probably representing the substrate of an important part of the hereditary characteristics; they are most likely permanent but generally only become visible in an ordinary microscope when the cell is dividing. They consist largely of nucleo-protein.

Cotylosaur: primitive reptile, similar to the stegocephalians, with a cranium with no temporal fossa and only one occipital condyle.

Crossopterygian: see p. 105.

Cynomorphs: catarrhines with a well-developed tail and quadruped gait.

Cytology: the study of living cells.

Cytomembrane: intracellular double membranes visible only in the electron microscope.

Desoxyribonucleic acid: (DNA); a nucleic acid is a compound of pentose sugar (sugar with five carbon atoms), phosphoric acid, and a nitrogenous base, forming macromolecules, usually nucleo-proteins, characteristic of all living things. In chromosomes it is found as DNA, of which desoxyribose is the sugar, and in other parts of the cell as RNA, ribonucleic acid, of which ribose is the sugar.

Dryopithecus: fossil ape widely found in the miocene and lower pliocene deposits of Europe and India; allied to the chimpanzees and gorilla, and to *Proconsul* of East Africa.

Epitaxis: property of some crystal structures of orientating the molecules of other substances in certain privileged directions in space.

Galaxy: mass of stars in the form of a flat disc which, seen from the earth, assumes the classic appearance of the Milky Way. The solar system, to which we belong, is part of the Galaxy and is placed about 25,000 light-years from its centre (in the constellation of Sagittarius), a little to the north of the galactic equator.

Gamma-rays: electro-magnetic radiation like X-rays but of considerably shorter wavelength.

Genotype: the hereditary constitution in terms of the set of genes in the germ cell of an organism, as contrasted with the set of characteristics manifested by the organism, which is the phenotype. It is possible for organisms to have the same genotype, but different phenotypes, because of differences in the influence of the environment, or the same phenotype but different genotypes, because of the dominant effect of similar genes.

Gliodic: term proposed by Bottazi to refer to protoplasm as a "fluid hydrogel"; that is, as a colloid like the gels, having an aqueous part and some fluidity.

"Good" species: a good species is one in which the morphological differences between it and those most nearly related to it are distinct and large enough to be recognized by all systematists, and accepted as of specific rank. This should apply to all examples, not just the types, so a good species should not intergrade with its neighbours through a series of intermediate forms.

Heterogeny: the birth of living things from non-living, inorganic matter.

Heterotrophic: organisms depending for their nutrition on organic matter, being incapable of subsisting on inorganic material alone; this organic food is directly or indirectly provided as a result of the activity of autotrophic organisms.

Homoeothermic: "warm-blooded", maintaining by some internal regulatory mechanism a constant body temperature, raised above that of the usual surroundings; characteristic of birds and mammals, as opposed to the reptiles, etc., which are poikilothermic or heterothermic. These are often called "cold-blooded', but poikilothermic means "of varying temperature", the blood temperature approximately following that of the environment.

Ichthyostegidae: stegocephalian (q.v.) batrachians with a cranium similar to that of crossopterygian fish.

Infra-micronic: less than one micron, a micron being one thousandth of a millimetre (10^{-4} cm.).

Macromolecules: molecules formed from a large number of atoms of different kinds, of a generally complex and often periodic structure.

Mendeleyev's Classification: classification of the chemical elements first proposed by the Russian chemist Dmitri Ivanovich Mendeleyev in 1869, which shows that chemically similar elements recur in a definite order if the elements are arranged in order of their atomic weights; it has since been shown that their properties depend on their atomic structure.

Mesology: the study of the relations between an organism and the environment; mesological—pertaining to the external environment.

Metamorphism: whole series of transformations by which the sedimentary deposits were submitted at great depth to various powerful forces (pressure, temperature, fusion of neighbouring rocks, etc.) and became both crystalline and stratified.

Metastable: a state theoretically unstable but capable of persisting indefinitely in the absence of any external disturbance.

Neoteny: generally, the persistence of the larval or early stage of development, either of a whole organism or of individual structures; more narrowly, the arrival at a state of sexual maturity of an organism otherwise in a larval or semi-developed form.

Nucleic acid: see Desoxyribonucleic acid.

Nucleo-protein: compounds of nucleic acid and protein.

Orogenesis: (etymologically) mountain-formation.

Phenotype: see Genotype.

Photosynthesis: synthesis of organic compounds, including carbohydrates, and, less directly, fats and proteins, from carbon dioxide and water using light energy absorbed by chlorophyll, and yielding oxygen as a by-product.

Plasmodium: multi-nucleate mass of protoplasm bounded by plasma membrane, of no definite size or shape.

Platyrrhines: New World monkeys with a broad nasal septum, and often having prehensile tails; e.g., marmoset.

Poikilothermic: "cold-blooded"; see Homoeothermic.

Protocaryota: organisms of a precellular degree of organization; i.e., bacteria and microbes, in the general sense.

Protoplasm: all within the membrane of a cell except large vacuoles and food particles; in animals and plants divided into nucleus and cytoplasm.

Racemic: properly, of flowering shoots, of an inflorescence consisting of an axis growing at the tip and flowers produced on side branches sprouting from below upwards. So of any similar symmetrical pattern, and here of a mixture of optically inverse molecules; these last are chemically similar but with their atoms so arranged in space that one is the mirror image of the other.

Stegocephalian: fossil amphibians having a completely bony covering to the head, unlike present-day amphibians.

Tachytelic: showing a high rate of change.

Taxonomy: science of classification of living things.

Telencephalon: foremost section of the brain, which gives rise to the cerebral hemispheres.

Theriodonts: theromorph reptiles with teeth clearly separated into incisors, canines and molars, with no palatines; the skull has a large temporal fossa, a palatine arch, and an occipital condyle which sometimes suggests a division into two.

Theromorphs: fossil reptiles of the Permian which, with the plesiosaurs, make up the synapsida, characterized by the fact that the skull has one temporal fossa on each side.

SELECT BIBLIOGRAPHY

In this series:
BIOT, René: *What is Life?*
CORTE, Nicolas: *The Origins of Man.*

CANNON, H. G.: *The Evolution of Living Things*, Manchester, University Press, 1958.

CLARK, W. E. Le Gros: *History of the Primates*, 4th edition, British Museum and Chicago, Chicago Univ. Press, 1954; *Fossil Evidence for Human Evolution*, Chicago, Univ. Press, 1955.

DOBZHANSKY, T. G.: *Genetics and the Origin of Species*, Oxford, Univ. Press, and New York, Columbia Univ. Press, 1951.

FOTHERGILL, P. G.: *Historical Aspects of Organic Evolution*, London, Hollis and Carter, 1952.

HOYLE, Fred: *The Nature of the Universe*, Oxford, Blackwell, and New York, Harper, 1950.

HUXLEY, J. S.: *Evolution, the Modern Synthesis*, London, Allen and Unwin, and New York, Harper, 1942.

JEPSON, G. L., SIMPSON, G. G., and MAYR, E. (Editors): *Genetics, Palaeontology and Evolution*, Princeton, N.J., Princeton Univ. Press, 1949.

MESSENGER, E. C.: *Evolution and Theology*, London, Burns Oates, 1931; *Theology and Evolution*, London, Sands, 1949, and Westminster, Md, Newman Press, 1952.

OPARIN, A. I.: *The Origin of Life on the Earth*, translated from Russian by Ann Synge, 3rd edition, Edinburgh, Oliver and Boyd, and New York, Academic Press, 1957.

SCHRÖDINGER, E.: *What is Life?*, Cambridge and New York, Cambridge Univ. Press.

SIMPSON, G. G.: *The Meaning of Evolution*, New Haven, Conn., Yale Univ. Press, 1949; *The Major Features of Evolution*, New York, Columbia Univ. Press, 1953.

TEILHARD DE CHARDIN, P.: *The Phenomenon of Man*, London, Collins, and New York, Harper and Brothers, 1959.

WHITTAKER, E. T.: *The Beginning and End of the World*, Oxford and New York, Oxford Univ. Press, 1942.